SPOTLIGHT on MUSIC

PIANO ACCOMPANIMENTS

Grade 6

Series Authors

Judy Bond	Betsy M. Henderson	Nancy L.T. Miller
René Boyer	John Jacobson	Ivy Rawlins
Margaret Campbelle-Holman	Michael Jothen	Susan Snyder
Emily Crocker	Chris Judah-Lauder	Gilberto D. Soto
Marilyn C. Davidson	Carol King	
Robert de Frece	Vincent P. Lawrence	**Kodály Contributing Consultant**
Virginia Ebinger	Ellen McCullough-Brabson	Sr. Lorna Zemke
Mary Goetze	Janet McMillion	

NOTE TO THE TEACHER

You asked for it—you got it! Now, for the first time ever, the new piano arrangements for Spotlight on Music™ replicate the vocal and instrumental arrangement on the song recordings. This time-saving feature ensures a seamless transition from the recorded performance to the classroom experience with respect to the harmonic structure, from, and style of the song.

For support in teaching choreography, use the following segments from the Grade-Level DVD:
- **John Jacobson**, which demonstrates selected songs' choreography in front, back, and split screen views.
- **Music Theatre International**, in which Broadway for Kids choreography is presented in several formats, including a slower tempo and a teaching segment of specific choreography details.

The Grade-Level DVD booklet offers additional support with a glossary of choreographed movements and terms related to stage movements.

Choreography notes for the songs in the Broadway for Kids musical are provided by Music Theatre International. Choreography notes for all other songs are written by John Jacobson.

The McGraw·Hill Companies

 **Macmillan McGraw-Hill**

Published by Macmillan/McGraw-Hill, of McGraw-Hill Education, a division of The McGraw-Hill Companies, Inc., Two Penn Plaza, New York, New York, 10121

Printed in the United States of America

ISBN: 0-02-295861-4

6 7 8 9 079 09

In the Spotlight Contents

Ev'ry Time I Feel the Spirit

African American Spiritual
Arranged by Moses Hogan
Piano Accompaniment by Carol Jay

Patriotic Medley

PUPIL'S PAGE H

Words by George M. Cohan, Woody Guthrie,
and Katharine Lee Bates
Piano Accompaniment by Mark Brymer

Step into the Spotlight

Hold flashlight under chin in R hand
They are off

PUPIL'S PAGE A

Words and Music by John Jacobson,
Emily Crocker, and John Higgins
Piano Accompaniment by Dean Crocker

1 group at a time: turn light on so it shines up and on face

1. Lis-ten to the world a-round you, There is mu-sic ev-'ry-where.___ Just

step out-side___ your door-way, and you can hear mu-sic in the air!___

Light on. Rainbow R arm with flashlight in a ripple from stage L to R

1. From the cit-y to the farm and field,___ to the
2. From the cit-y to the farm and field,___ there's a

The Wind Beneath My Wings

PUPIL'S PAGE E

Words and Music by Larry Henley and Jeff Silbar
Arranged by Gordon Goodwin
Piano accompaniment by Ben Scholz

1. It must have been cold there in my shad - ow,
2. So I was the cold one with all the glo - ry,
3. It might have ap - peared to go un - no - ticed,

to nev - er have sun_____ light on your face.
while you were the one_____ with all the strength.
but I've got it all_____ here in my heart.

The Wind Beneath My Wings, From the original motion picture BEACHES, Words and Music by Larry Healey and Jeff Silban. © 1982 WARNER HOUSE OF MUSIC and WB GOLD MUSIC CORP. All Rights Reserved.

You were con - tent to let me shine,_____
A beau - ti - ful face with - out a name,_____
I want you to know I know the truth,

you al - ways walked a step___ be - hind.
a beau - ti - ful
I would be

smile to hide___ the pain.
noth - ing with___ out you.

Did you ev - er know_

that you're my he - ro, and ev-'ry-thing I would like to be?

I can fly high - er than an ea - gle, 'cause you are the wind be-neath my wings.

Al lado de mi cabaña
(Beside My Cottage)

PUPIL'S PAGE 141

Spanish Folk Song
Piano Accompaniment by Dean Crocker

Spanish: Al la - do de___ mi ca - ba - ña ten - go|lu - na huer - ta y un -
English: Be - side my cot - tage, I have a gar - den with straw - ber - ries___

___ ma - dro ñal.___ Con mi ca - ba - ña y la huer - ta - le - ré,
___ by the door.___ With my small cot - tage, my gar - den, and my

y los ma - dro ños, le - ré, ¿qué quie - ro mas?___ mas?___
straw - ber - ries I know that I'll nev - er want more!___ more!___

All Ye Who Music Love

Words by Thomas Olihant
Music by Baldassare Donato
Arranged by Carol Kelley
Piano Accompaniment by Dean Crocker

1. All ye who mu - sic, All ye who mu - sic love, And would its pleas - ures prove; All
2. Come, lads and lass - es, Come, lads and lass - es all, O - bey the tune - ful call; Come,

ye who mu - sic, All ye who mu - sic love, And
lads and lass - es, Come lads and lass - es all, O -

would its pleas - ures prove; } O come to us who cease not, cease not dai -
bey the tune - ful call; } O come, O come to us who cease not, cease not dai -

ly; Cease not dai - ly, cease__ not dai - ly; From morn 'til eve to war - ble

ly; Cease not dai - ly, cease__ not dai - ly; From morn 'til

gai - ly, war - ble gai - ly, From morn 'til eve to war - ble gai - ly.

eve to war - ble gai - ly, 'Til eve___ to war - ble gai - ly.

Fa la la la la la, Fa la la la la la la la la la. Fa la la

la la la la la la la. Fa la la la la la la la la. la.

Alleluia

PUPIL'S PAGE 186

Wolfgang Amadeus Mozart
Piano Accompaniment by Dean Crocker

Introduction not on Pupil's page

Al - le - lu - ia, Al -

le - lu - ia,_____ Al - le - lu - ia, Al - le - lu - ia.

Al - le - lu - ia, Al - le - lu - ia, _____ Al - le - lu - ia, Al -

le - lu - ia. Al - le - lu - ia, Al -

le - lu - ia.

America

PUPIL'S PAGE 388

Words by Henry Carey
Music by Samuel F. Smith
Piano Accompaniment by MMH

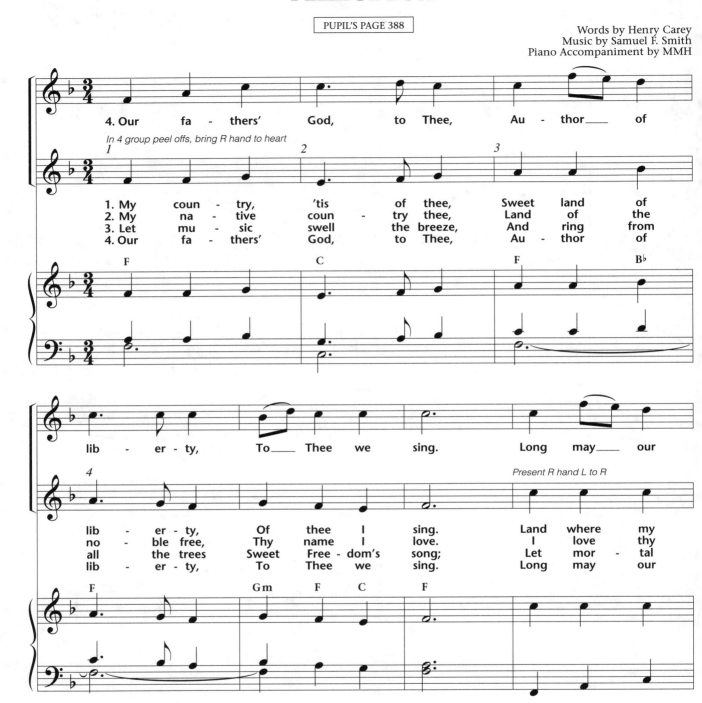

Descant found in Teacher's Edition

8

land   be bright   With   Free - dom's   ho - ly light;

Put fists on hips

fa - thers died,   Land   of   the   Pil - grim's pride,
rocks   and   rills,   Thy   woods   and   that   tem - pled hills;
tongues   a - wake,   Let   all   that   breathe   par - take,
land   be bright   With   Free - dom's   ho - ly light;

F   C7

Pro - tect   us   by thy___ might,   Great   God___ our   King!

Look from low to high

Raise R fist

Open R hand and let it drop slowly to side, then bring it to your heart for a final pose

From   ev - 'ry___   moun - tain - side   Let___   free - dom   ring.
My   heart___ with___   rap - ture thrills   Like___   that   a - bove.
Let   rocks___ their___   si - lence break,   The___   sound   pro - long.
Pro - tect___ us___   by   thy might,   Great___   God,   our   King!

F   B♭   F   C   F

Angelina

Words and Music by Irving Burgie
Piano Accompaniment by Dean Crocker

Introduction not on Pupil's page

(drums)

Verse 1

1. It's so

long since I've___ been home; seems like there's no place___ to roam. I've

Wipe hands like "safe"

2nd time to Coda ⊕

Coda

Salute with R hand to forehead

Burst R hand from forehead high to low

All clasp begging hands for final pose

com - ing home from sea.

A–Rovin'

PUPIL'S PAGE 319

Sea Chantey
Adapted and Arranged by Emily Crocker
Piano Accompaniment by Dean Crocker

11
Am - ster - dam there lived a maid, and for her smiles a sai - lor stayed.
took this fair maid for a walk, and they had such a love - ly talk.
Am - ster - dam there lived a maid.
took this fair maid for a walk,
And I will
A♭ E♭ A♭ E♭/B♭ A♭/B♭ B♭7
15
f
I'll rove no more with you, fair maid. A -
go no more a - rov - in' with you, my fair maid.
E♭ B♭7 E♭ A♭ E♭/B♭ Fm7/B♭ B♭7 E♭

rov - in', a - rov - in', since rov - in's been my ru - i - in.* I'll

A - rov - in', a - rov - in', I'll go no more a -

rove no more with you, fair maid. maid. And

rov - in' with you, my fair maid. maid. And

roo-eye-in

he did tell her sto-ries true, mark well what I do say, And

he did tell her sto-ries true, mark well what I do say, and

E   B7   E   B7   E   B7   E   B/D♯ E

he did tell her sto-ries true of the gold they found in Tim-buk-tu.

he did tell her sto-ries true   And I___ will___

A   E   A   E/B A/B B7

you, fair maid.

you my fair maid.

But when his cash was gone and spent, mark well what I do say.

But when his cash was gone and spent, mark well what I do say. But

20

rov - in', since rov-in's been my ru - i - in.   I'll rove no more with

a - rov - in',   I'll go no more a - rov - in' with

E   A   E/B A/B B7   E   B7   E   A

you, fair   maid.   I'll go no more a - rov - in' with you fair maid!

you, my fair   maid.   I'll go no more a - rov - in' with you fair maid!

E/B   F♯m7/B B7   E   E   A   E   B7   E

Barbry Ellen

PUPIL'S PAGE 208

English Folk Song
Piano Accompaniment by Dean Crocker

1. All in the mer - ry month of__ May, When the green buds
2. He sent his ser - vant to the__ town To the place where
3. So slow - lie, slow - lie she got__ up And slow - ly
4. Oh yes, I'm low, I'm ver - y__ low, And death is
5. Oh yes, you're low and ver - y__ low, And death is

they were__ swell - in', Young__ Wil - liam Green on his death bed__
she was__ dwell - in', Say - in', Mas - ter's sick and he sends for__
she came a nigh__ him And__ all she__ said when__ she got__
on me__ dwell - in', No_____ bet - ter, no bet - ter I'll ev - er
on you__ dwell - in', No_____ bet - ter, no bet - ter you'll nev - er

lay, For the love of Bar - bry__ El - len.
you If your name is Bar - bry__ El - len.
there young__ man I be - lieve_____ you're__ dy - in'.
be If I can't wed Bar - bry__ El - len.
be For you can't wed Bar - bry__ El - len.

Bashana Haba'ah
(In the Year to Come)

PUPIL'S PAGE 360

Words by Ehud Manor
Music by Nurit Hirsh
Arranged by V. Pasternak
Edited by Henry Leck
Piano Accompaniment by Robert Houghton

Belle qui tiens ma vie
(My Love, You Hold My Life)

PUPIL'S PAGE 99

Words and Music by Thoinot Arbeau
Piano Accompaniment by Dean Crocker

French: Bel - le qui tiens ma vi - e cap - ti - ve dans tes yeux
English: My love, you hold my life_____ a cap - tive in your eyes.

Qui mas l'â - me ra - vi - é d'un sou - ris gra - ci - eux
As if a lit - tle mouse had been cap - tured in the house.

Viens tôt me se - cou - rir ou me___ fau - dra mou - rir,
Come, soon and res - cue me, Love, has - ten and Set me free!

F   Dm   Gm   Cm   D   B♭   C   Gm   D sus 4   D   G (no 3rd)

Viens tôt me se - cou - rir ou me___ fau - dra mou - rir.
Come soon and res - cue me, Love, has - ten and set me free.

B♭   F   Dm   Gm   Cm   D   B♭   A m/C   Gm   D sus 4   D   G (no 3rd)

Blue Suede Shoes

PUPIL'S PAGE 236

Words and Music by Carl Lee Perkins
Piano Accompaniment by Dean Crocker

Rockabilly

Face upstage
1/3 face front with R index finger up   *2nd 1/3 face front with 2 fingers up*   *3rd 1/3 face front with 3 fingers up*

Well, it's one for the mon-ey, two for the show, three to get read-y, now

All point high to low with rubber legs   *Step L*   *Stomp R foot across front*   *Step R*   *Stomp L foot across*   *Step L*   *Stomp R foot across 3 times*

go, cat, go! But don't you step on my Blue Suede Shoes.

Point R hand L to R at shoulder level

Well you can do an-y-thing___ but lay off of my Blue Suede Shoes.___

29

Bop 'til You Drop

PUPIL'S PAGE 87

Words and Music by Douglas Colvin and John Cummings
Piano Accompaniment by Dean Crocker

Create a group starburst pose
so that all can be seen

Dance,   dance!_____   D - d - dance!

Bulbes
('Taters)

PUPIL'S PAGE 280

Yiddish Folk Song
English Words by Jacob Sloan
Piano Accompaniment by Dean Crocker

Camelot

PUPIL'S PAGE 310

Words by Alan Jay Lerner
Music by Frederick Loewe
Piano Accompaniment by Dean Crocker

Pupil's Edition repeats

And there's a le - gal lim - it to the snow here in Cam - e - lot. 2. The win - ter is for - bid - den till De - cem - ber, and ex - its March the sec - ond on the

dot.   By or - der sum - mer lin - gers through Sep -

tem -   ber   in Cam - e - lot.

Cam - e - lot!

Cam - e - lot!   I know it sounds a bit bi - zarre,

But in Cam - e - lot,

Cam - e - lot,   that's how con - di - tions are.

3. The rain may nev-er fall till af-ter sun-down. By eight the morn-ing fog must dis-ap-pear. In short, there's sim-ply not a

more con - gen - ial spot for hap - p'ly - ev - er - af - ter - ing than

here in Cam - e -

lot!

Canon

Music by Luigi Cherubini
Traditional English Words
Piano Accompaniment by Dean Crocker

42

wrong,   if you sing, "La ti ti do."   The ga-mut you will   run,   and then your song is

mi   *fa*   *so,*   Oh   sing   a   song,   You can sing it loud and

D   G(add9)/D   D   A 7sus4   D   A 7sus4/D

done.   *Ti*   *do*   *so*   *mi*   *so*

long   and you nev - er will go wrong,   if you sing, "La ti ti do."   The ga-mut you will

D   A 9   D   G(add9)/D   D   A 7sus4

run, and then your song is done. Ti do so

mi so do.

Cape Cod Chantey

PUPIL'S PAGE 258

New England Sea Chantey
Piano Accompaniment by Dean Crocker

Hearty

Introduction not in Pupil's Edition

Verse

Solo ... *Group*

1. Cape Cod girls they have no combs,
2. Cape Cod boys they have no sleds,
3. Cape Cod men they have no sails,
4. Cape Cod wives they have no pins,

Heave a - way, heave a -

Solo ... *Group*

way.
They comb their hair with cod - fish bones,
They slide down - hill on cod - fish heads,
They sail their boats with cod - fish tails,
They pin their boats with cod - fish fins,

We are bound for Aus - tra - lia!

Refrain

Heave a-way my bul-ly, bul-ly boys, Heave a - way! Heave a - way!

Heave a-way and don't you make a noise, We are bound for Aus - tra - lia!

Captain Jinks

PUPIL'S PAGE 266

Traditional Dance Tune
Piano Accompaniment by Dean Crocker

Brisk

Introduction not on Pupil's page

1. I'm Cap - tain Jinks of the
2. I joined my corps___ when
3. The first day I___ went
4. My tail - or's bills___ came
5. ℐ Cap - tain Jinks___ came

Horse Ma-rines, I feed my horse on corn and beans, And of - ten live be -
twen - ty one, Of course I thought it cap-i - tal fun, When the en-e - my came, of
out to drill, The bu - gle made me feel quite ill, At the bal - ance step, my
in so fast, Forced me one day to leave at last, And la - dies, too, no
home last night,___ Pass your part - ner by the right,___ Swing your neigh - bor

yond my means, Though a cap - tain in the Ar - my. I
course I run, For I'm not cut out for the Ar - my. When
hat it fell, And that would - n't do for the Ar - my. The
more did cast sheep's___ eyes at me in the Ar - my. My
so po - lite, For___ that's the style in the Ar - my. ℐ

47

teach young la - dies how to dance, how to dance, how to dance, I
I left home, Ma - ma, she cried, Ma - ma, she cried, Ma - ma, she cried, When
of - fi - cers they all did shout, all cried out, all cried out, The
cred - i - tors at me did shout, at me did shout, at me did shout, My
All join hands and cir - cle left, cir - cle left, cir - cle left,

C   G   D 7   G

teach young la - dies how to dance, For I'm the star of the
I left home, Ma - ma, she cried, "He's not cut out for the
of - fi - cers they all did shout, "Oh, that's the cure for the
cred - i - tors at me did shout, "Why, kick him out of the
All join hands and cir - cle left, For that's the style of the

C   G   A   A/C#

Refrain

Ar - my. ___
Ar - my!" ___
Ar - my!" ___ } I'm ___ Cap - tain Jinks of the Horse Ma - rines, I feed my horse on
Ar - my!" ___
Ar - my. ___

D   G   C   G   Am   D7

corn and beans, And of - ten live be - yond the means of a Cap - tain in the Ar - my.

Carol from an Irish Cabin

PUPIL'S PAGE 408

Words by Ruth Durand
Music by Dale Wood
Piano Accompaniment by Dean Crocker

Introduction not on Pupil's page

1. The
2. The
3. So

cold wind blows o - ver the heath - er,_____ The salt wind blows o - ver the sea,_____ The_____
clean snow falls soft - ly, falls soft - ly,_____ The snow crys - tals cov - er the moor._____ Let_____
let there be no fear of dark - ness,_____ And let there be no fear of sea;_____ Let the

harsh wind blows down from the moun - tains,_____ And blows a white Christ - mas to me._____
wan - der - ers lost and grown wea - ry,_____ Find wel - come at my cab - in door._____
star guide the lost and for - sak - en, Safe o - ver the moor - lands to me._____

Charleston

PUPIL'S PAGE 112

Music by James P. Johnson
Words by Cecil Mack
Piano Accompaniment by Dean Crocker

Bright two *Full Charleston or just Charleston hands*

Charles - ton__ Charles - ton__ Made in__ Car-o - li - na

Chugs

Some dance,__ some prance,__ I'll say__ there's no-thing fin - er than the

Full Charleston or just Charleston hands

Charles - ton,__ Charles - ton,__ lord how__ you can shuf - fle__

51

ev - 'ry step___ you do   leads to some - thing new,   man I'm tell - ing you

It's a la - pa-zoo,   buck dance,___   wing dance,___   We'll be___ a back

num - ber___   but the Charles - ton___   the new   Charles - ton,___

Charlotte Town

PUPIL'S PAGE 261

American Folk Song
Piano Accompaniment by Dean Crocker

54

sor - ry? Cai - ro, loved her. Good-bye, good-bye, Ain't ya' might - y sor - ry? Go - in' down to Cai - ro, Oh,_____ how I loved her.

C/G G   G   D   G   C/G G

Good - bye, Li - za   Jane.   Jane.   3. The   Jane.

G   D   G   G   G

Chiribim

PUPIL'S PAGE 57

Traditional Yiddish Song
Piano Accompaniment by Dean Crocker

Tempo (♩ = 84)

Introduction not on Pupil's page

Pronunciation: uxɛ sheo maɾ le xɑ do di tom ɾu kul xem chi ɾi bi ɾi bim

oi chi ri bi ri bi ri bim bom bom   oi chi ri bi ri bi ri bim bom bom

Chíu, chíu, chíu

PUPIL'S PAGE 172

Uruguayan Folk Song
English Version by MMH
Piano Accompaniment by Mark Brymer

Introduction not on Pupil's page

Spanish: **Can** - ta, can-ta, pa-ja-
English: **Can** - ta, can-ta pa-ja-

ri - to._____ Can - ta, can-ta tu can - ción,
ri - to._____ Sing the songs that cheer me so.

Mi - ra que la vi-da_es tris-te y tu can-tar me_a-le-gra_el co-ra-
See, my life is full of sor-row, your mer-ry sing - ing sets my heart a-

59

zon.
glow.

Chí - u, chí - u, chí - u, chí - u,_____
Chí - u, chí - u, chí - u, chí - u,_____

chí - u, chí - u, chí - u, chí - u._____
chí - u, chí - u, chí - u, chí - u._____

Can - ta, can - ta pa - ja -
Can - ta, can - ta pa - ja -

ri - to.
ri - to.

Que tu can - tar me_a - le - gra_el co - ra -
Your mer - ry sing - - - ing sets my heart a -

Refrain
zon. Con tus gor - je - os, con tu tri - nar, Des - pier - ta‿el
glow. Your mer - ry chirp - ing; your roun - de - lay, You bring the
B♭ F E♭ F B♭
al - ba, la no - che ya se va. Con tus gor - je - os, con tu tri -
dawn - ing, the shad - ows fade a - way, Your mer - ry chirp - ing; your roun - de -
E♭ F B♭ E♭ F
nar, Des - pier - ta‿el al - ba, la no - che ya se va.
lay. You bring the dawn - ing, the shad - ows fade a - way.
B♭ E♭ F B♭

Choo Choo Ch' Boogie

PUPIL'S PAGE 180

Words and Music by Vaughn Horton,
Denver Darling and Milton Gabler
Piano Accompaniment by Dean Crocker

Face L, add on train step in 6 groups

Choo - Choo___   Choo - Choo - Ch - Boo - gie,   Woo - Woo___   Woo-

___ woo ch' boo - gie   Choo - Choo___   Choo - Choo - Ch - Boo - gie

1.
Repeat R thumb over R shoulder in a ripple from L to R

Take me right back to   the   track,   Jack!___

2.
R thumb over R shoulder in peel off L to R

2. You   Take me right back to the   track,   Jack!___

The Coasts of High Barbary

PUPIL'S PAGE 329

Sea Song
Arranged by Jeanne Julseth-Heinrich
Piano Accompaniment by Dean Crocker

mast a - way! Blow ye winds, blow High_____ Bar - ba -

pi-rate's mast a - way! A - sail-ing down all on the coasts of High_____ Bar - ba -

Gm   Dm   Gm   F   E♭   Dm

mf   L.H.

ry!_____ I'm bound,_____ I'm bound for the sea!_____ Yo

ry!_____ I'm bound,_____ I'm bound for the sea!_____ Yo

Gm   F   E♭   Dm   Gm

ho!_____ Yo ho! It's off we go!_____

ho!_____ Yo ho! It's off we go!_____

Come and Sing Together

PUPIL'S PAGE 281

Traditional Hungarian Melody
Piano Accompaniment by Carol Jay

you don't need a cent, you see, so come and sing to-geth - er!

me, you don't need a cent, you see, so come and sing to -

If you'd dance then you must have boots of shin-ing leath - er!

geth - er! If you'd dance then you must have boots of shin-ing leath-er!

Comedy Tonight

PUPIL'S PAGE 204

Words and Music by Steven Sondheim
Piano Accompaniment by Mark Brymer

com-e-dy to - night! Noth-ing with kings, noth-ing with crowns.
com-e-dy to - night! Noth-ing of Gods, noth-ing of Fate.

Bring on the lov - ers, li - ars and clowns!__ Old sit - u - a - tions,
Weigh-ty af - fairs will just have to wait.__ Noth-ing that's for - mal,

new com - pli - ca - tions, Noth-ing por - ten-tous or po - lite:_____
noth-ing that's nor - mal. No re - ci - ta-tions to re - cite!_____

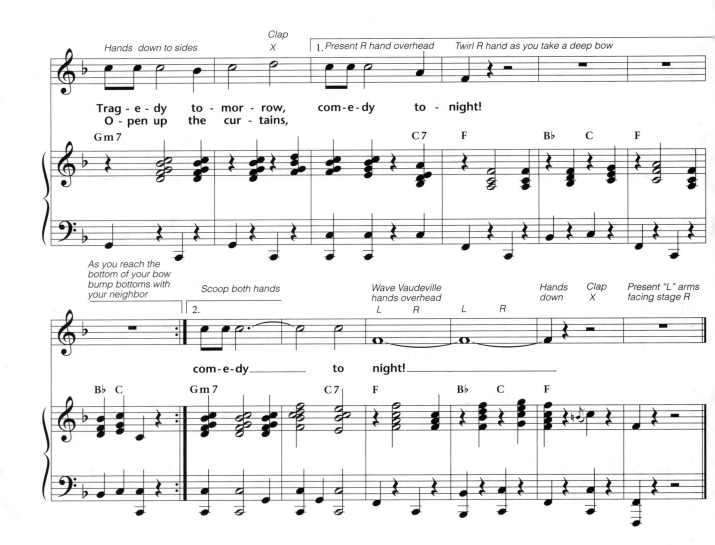

Conga

PUPIL'S PAGE 34

Words and Music by Enrique Garcia
Piano Accompaniment by Dean Crocker

Interludes not shown in accompaniment

Down L   Up R

___ the rhy - thm of the mu - sic get - ting stron - ger. Don't___

E m

Low to high   Present high

___ you fight it till you've tried it; do that con - ga beat.

D

Verse

"California Raisins"

L   R   L   R

Flop elbows at shoulder height 2 times per measure

1   2   1   2

1. Ev' - ry - bod - y___   gath - er 'round now;___
2. Don't you wor - ry___   if you can't dance;___
3. It's the rhy - thm___   of the is - land___
4. If you want to___   do the con - ga,___

E m   D

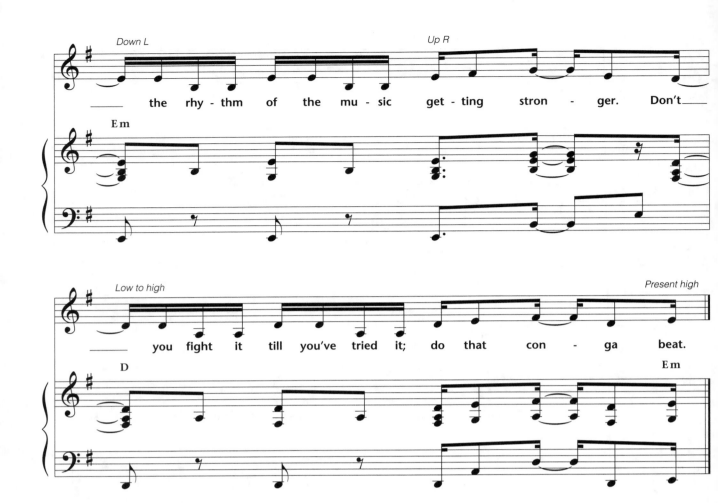

the rhy-thm of the mu-sic get-ting stron-ger. Don't

you fight it till you've tried it; do that con-ga beat.

Cripple Creek

PUPIL'S PAGE 372

American Fiddle Tune
Arranged by Emily Crocker
Piano Accompaniment by Dean Crocker

1. John-ny's got a gal at the head of the creek,

Just like an ap-ple from the tree,

Goes up to see her 'bout the mid-dle of the week.

Scoop L hand to waist level · Scoop R hand to waist level · Fist to hips · Plié once

2. Crip-ple Creek's wide and Crip-ple Creek's deep, he'll wade Crip-ple Creek be - fore he sleeps.

2. Crip-ple Creek's wide and Crip-ple Creek's deep, he'll wade Crip-ple Creek be - fore he sleeps.

Hands on knees · Stand up straight

Rolls his britch-es up to his knees,___ He'll wade Crip-ple Creek when - ev-er he please.

Rolls his britch-es up to his knees,___ He'll wade Crip-ple Creek when - ev-er he please.

4 whack attacks

Go - in' up Crip - ple Creek, go - in' up to have a lit-tle fun.

Go-in' up Crip-ple Creek, go-in' in a run, go-in' up Crip-ple Creek to have a lit-tle fun.

1st time *mf*
2nd time *mp*
3rd time *p*
Observe repeat on D.S.

Part I: 4 whack attacks
Part II: Pat R let on off beats 8 times then L leg 8 times
On the repeat, voice parts switch actions

Go - in' up Crip - ple Creek, go - in' up to see his girl.

Go-in' up Crip-ple Creek, go-in' in a whirl, go-in' up Crip-ple Creek to see his girl.

Go - in' up Crip - ple Creek, go - in' up to have a lit-tle fun.

Go-in' up Crip-ple Creek, go-in' in a run, go-in' up Crip-ple Creek to have a lit-tle fun.

Go - in' up Crip - ple Creek, go - in' up to see his girl.

Go-in' up Crip-ple Creek, go-in' in a whirl, go-in' up Crip-ple Creek to see his girl.

mel.

Stop with arms folded over chest

Tap forehead with R index finger 2 times

3. Half - way there he stops to rest, thinks a - bout the gal that he loves best.

3. Half - way there he stops to rest, thinks a - bout the gal that he loves best.

mel.

85

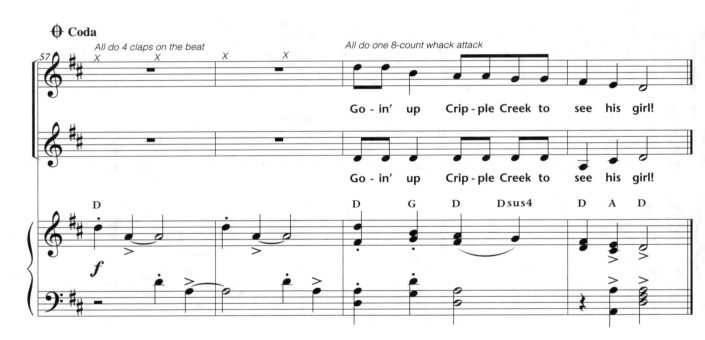

Cum-ma-la Be-stay

PUPIL'S PAGE 370

Words and Music by Donny Burke, Jerry Vance and Terry Philips
Arranged by Michael Jothen
Piano Accompaniment by MMH

*Part 2 remains in bass clef in piano acccompaniment book

87

friends and I we gath-er round,___ We dance and sing to the cum-ma-la sound.

All Cum-ma-la sound, *Solo* Cum-ma-la sound. *All* Ev-'ry-bod-y forms a cir - cle;___

All Cum-ma-la sound, *All* Ev-'ry-bod-y forms a cir - cle;___

Now some-bod-y jumps in-side.___

Now some-bod-y jumps in-side.___

Dancing in the Street

PUPIL'S PAGE 84

Words and Music by Marvin Gaye,
Ivy Hunter and William Stevenson
Piano Accompaniment by Dean Crocker

Tempo (♩ = 120)

Introduction not on Pupil's page

Feet apart
Fists to hips
with elbows back

Sweep both hands
from L to R with palms
down at waist level

Fists back to
hips as before

Step L   Double clap Step R   1 clap

Call - ing out___ a-round___ the world, "Are you read - y for a brand new beat?"

Repeat measure 3   Fists back to hips   Point R hand up high   Repeat measures 3 & 4 (double claps)

Sum-mer's here___ and the time is right   for danc-ing___ in the streets.

Temptation pushes

Temptation pushes   clap

They're danc - ing in Chi - ca - go,___   down in   New Or - leans,___

E 7

Point R hand up, feet apart   *Lower pointed hand*   *Reach both hands to audience*   *Sway snap*

up in New York Cit - y.   All we need___ is mu - sic,   sweet mu-

E 7   A   Em   A 7

Feet apart
Ripple R rainbow arm from stage L to R

- sic.   There'll be mu - sic ev - 'ry-where.___   There'll be

the world_ they'll be danc-ing._ They're danc - ing in the street.

Dandansoy

PUPIL'S PAGE 356

Traditional Visayan Folk Song
Piano Accompaniment by Dean Crocker

Tenderly (♩ = 100)

ling   kon i - kaw hid-la - won,_____   Ang Pa - yao   i -mo

lang lan - ta - won._____   Dan - dan -

soy,   Dan - dan soy._____

Dere Geliyor
(River Overflowing)

PUPIL'S PAGE 232

Tempo (♪ = 132)

Introduction not on Pupil's page

Traditional Turkish Folk Song
Piano Accompaniment by Dean Crocker

101

Bi - zim dü - ğün Za - man ya - le - le - lel - lim.
Tell me, tell me when, oh when will our wed-ding be.

Em   D   Em

Coda
3.   D.C.

ya - le - le - lel - lim.
will our wed-ding be.

Em

Derry Ding Dong Dason

PUPIL'S PAGE 249

English Canon
Piano Accompaniment by Dean Crocker

103

Didn't It Rain

PUPIL'S PAGE 345

Traditional Spiritual
Adapted and Arranged by Emily Crocker
Piano Accompaniment by Dean Crocker

With Energy (♩ = 104)

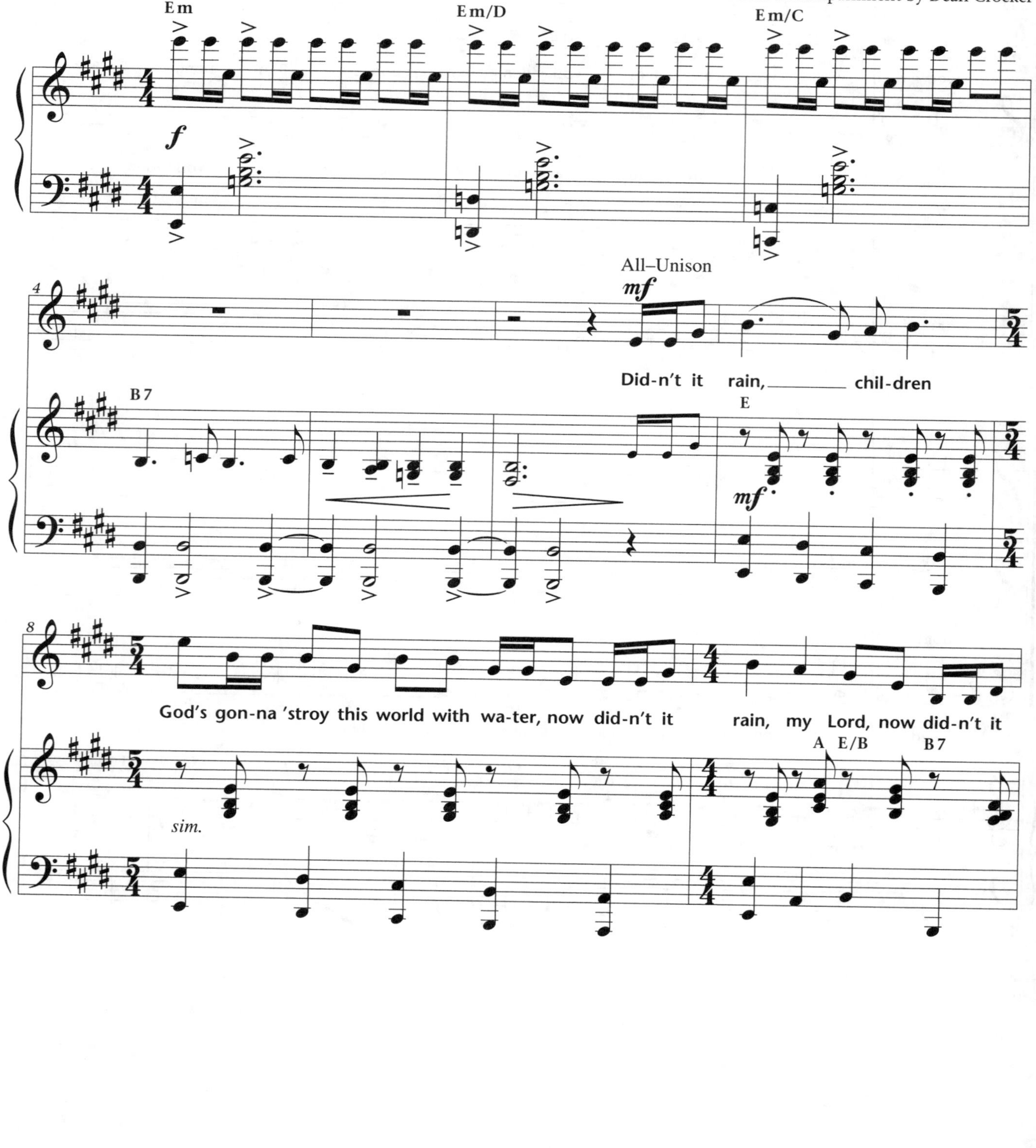

Em
Em/D
Em/C
f
All–Unison
mf
Did-n't it rain, children
B7
E
mf
God's gon-na 'stroy this world with wa-ter, now did-n't it rain, my Lord, now did-n't it
sim.
A E/B
B7

rain, rain,— rain.— Well, it rained for-ty days and it rained for-ty nights, there

was-n't no land no-where in sight.— God sent a ra-ven to car-ry the news, He

spread his wings and a-way he flew.— Did-n't it

rain,_____ chil-dren, God's gon-na 'stroy this world with wa-ter, now did-n't it

Did-n't it rain, did-n't it rain, did-n't it rain,

rain, my Lord, now did-n't it rain, rain,___ rain.___

rain, rain, did-n't it, did-n't it rain, rain,___ rain.___ Well, it

For-ty days, for-ty nights,

rained for-ty days 'n' for-ty nights with-out stop-pin',

rain, _____ chil-dren, God's gon-na 'stroy this world with wa-ter, now did-n't it

Did-n't it rain, did-n't it rain, did-n't it rain,

rain, my Lord, now did-n't it rain, rain, _____ rain. Did-n't it rain, did-n't it rain, did-n't it

rain, rain, did-n't it, did-n't it, rain, rain, _____ rain. Did-n't it rain, did-n't it rain, did-n't it

rain,_____ rain,_____ did-n't it rain!

rain,_____ rain,_____ did-n't it

Do Lord

PUPIL'S PAGE 260

African American Spiritual
Piano Accompaniment by Dean Crocker

Do Lord, O do Lord, O do re-mem-ber me. Do Lord, O do Lord, O do re-mem-ber me.

Do Lord, O do Lord, O do re-mem-ber me. Way be-yond the blue.

114

Doctor Jazz

PUPIL'S PAGE 378

Words and Music by John Jacobson and Steve Zegree
Piano Accompaniment by Dean Crocker

1. Have you heard who's new in town,___ the hip - pest new M. D.?
2. If by chance you caught the blues,___ your back beat just won't kick.

Ev' - ry time you're feel - in' down,___ he starts you
If your life is all bad news___ and___ your

116

Snap fingers of R hand on offbeats   *Wipe like "safe" in baseball*   *Flick both hands 4 times from low to high*

Doc - tor Jazz,___ it's not at all sur-pris-in'. got me an ap-point-ment on

Wipe like "safe" and plié   **to Coda**   *Truckin' fingers as you walk in a circle around yourself to the L*

Sat - ur-day night.___

Face L and wipe like "safe"   Clap   *Face R and wipe like "safe"*   *Shimmy jazz hands*

Doc - tor Jazz!___ What he haz!___ A su - per - cal - i - clin - ic and some

118

razz - a - ma - tazz.___ He likes___ to swing, and he likes___ to bop. And

af - ter ev'- ry date I get a lol - li - pop!___ He's got a cure for ev' - ry thing.___ Just

o - pen up your mouth and sing: ah - ah - ah. O - pen up your mouth and

Shimmy jazz hands

Face L and wipe like "safe"

Clap
X

Face R and wipe like "safe"

Hold stomach facing front

Plié

Sway snap

Claps "opera" hands

Plié

119

Interlude not included in accompaniment

Doing the Latest Rag

PUPIL'S PAGE 314

Words and Music by Maury Yeston
Piano Accompaniment by Dean Crocker

Introduction not in Pupil's Edition

1. Ev - 'ry - one up___ and out, fol - low the band___ and shout,

"Is - n't it a love - ly day!" Yes! Watch - ing all the la - dies in Pa -

Pupil's Edition repeats

ri - sian fash - ion on dis - play.

121

2. Young Mis - ter Hart - ley is play - ing quite smart - ly in

rhy - thm that could nev - er lag! It's a

mu - si - cal treat___ to hear a band with a beat___ per - form - ing

Part I

their lat - est rag! Come on and dance with me please,___

doors it's a thrill,_____ keeps you har - dy and health - i - er still._____

rag - time, rag -

E7sus   E7   G/A

_____ Take a part - ner if you dare!_____

time   now!_____

A9   F7

Ev - 'ry-one is burst-ing with e - mo - tion! Danc-ing as we cross the might - y

Eb   Edim   Bb   Eb   Edim

ƒ

o - cean! Has - n't it been ab - so - lute - ly great to dance the lat -

est rag! _____

Doney Gal

PUPIL'S PAGE 115

American Cowboy Song
Piano Accompaniment by Dean Crocker

gone at the break of day, Driv - ing the do - gies on their

wea - ry way. It's rain or shine, sleet or snow,

Me and my Don - ey Gal are bound to go. Yes, rain or shine,

sleet or snow, Me and my Don - ey Gal are on the go.

Down by the Riverside

Traditional African-American Spiritual
Arranged by Rollo Dilworth

Upbeat Gospel Swing (♩ = 132)

stud - y   war   no   more.___

stud - y   war   no   more,___   stud - y   war   no

F#dim7 Gm7 Am7 G7   C(add9)   A7 Dm7   C9   F   Gm

___   I ain't gon-na stud -y   war no more,___   I ain't gon - na   stud -y   war no more,___

more,   stud - y   war   no   more,___

F7/A B7(♭5)   B♭7   E7(♭5) F(add2)   A7

Earth Child

PUPIL'S PAGE 426

Words and Music by Sharon Burch
Piano Accompaniment by Larry Moore

133

peace,_____ With all the beau - ty that_____ sur - rounds me.

D.S. al Fine

El charro
(The Cowboy)

PUPIL'S PAGE 278

Mexican Folk Song
English Version by MMH
Piano Accompaniment by Carol Jay

Spanish: Es - ta - ba_un cha - rro sen - ta - do_____ en las
English: A mourn - ful cow - boy was sit - ting_____ on the

tran - cas de un cor - ral._____
rail - ing be - side a cor - ral._____

Su ma - yor - do - mo le di - ce:_____ "No_es - tés
Then came his fore - man to tell him, "Don't be un -

tris - te, Ni - co - las."_____
hap - py Ni - co - las."_____

• This page intentionally left blank to facilitate page turns. •

El tambor
(The Drum)

PUPIL'S PAGE 222

Panamanian Folk Song
Spanish words by José-Luis Orozco
English words by MMH
Piano Accompaniment by Bill and Pat Medley

Refrain

Spanish: El tam - bor, el tam - bor, el tam - bor de a - le - grí - a. Yo quie - ro que tú me lle - ves el tam - bor de a - le - grí - a.

English: El tam - bor, el tam - bor, el tam - bor, the drum of glad-ness, I want you to give me the drum, el tam - bor, the drum of glad - ness.

138

El tecolote
(The Owlet)

PUPIL'S PAGE 392

Mexican Folk Song
English Words by Linda Worsley
Piano Accompaniment by Larry Moore

Introduction not on Pupil's page

Spanish: Te - co - lo - te de Gua - da - ña, pá - ja - ro ma - dru - ga-
English: Lit - tle owl of Gua - da - ña cries. wak - ful - ly watch - ing the

dor. Te - co - lo - te de Gua - da - ña, pá - ja - ro ma - dru - ga-
night, Lit - tle owl of Bua - da - ña flies. And my poor heart would take

dor. Quién tu - vie - ra tus a - li - tas, quien tu - vie - ra tus a-
flight. With your wings I would go fly - ing, With your wings I would go

li - tas, quién tu - vie - ra____ tus a - li - tas   pa - ra   ir   a   ver a   mi _ a -
fly - ing, With your wings I'd____ fly   to   see her,   I   would   fly   a - way to my

mor._____   Cu - cu - ri - cú   ri - cú   ri - cú,   cu - cu - ri -
love._____   Hoo   cu - ri - cu, Hoo_____ Hoo_____   hoo - cu - ri -

cú   ri - cú   ri - cu   cu - cu - ri - cú   ri - cú   ri - cú,_____   po - bre -
cu, Hoo_____ hoo_____   hoo cu - ri - cu. Hoo_____ hoo,_____   cu - ri -

ci -   to te - co - lo - te_____ ya   se   can - só de vo - lar._____
cu   Hoo_____ cu - ri - cu_____ cu - ri - cu,   Hoo cu - ri - cu.

Elijah Rock

PUPIL'S PAGE 52

African American Spiritual
Arranged by René Boyer-Alexander
Piano Accompaniment by Larry Moore

E - li - jah rock, shout, shout!___ E - li - jah rock, com - in' up Lord.

D.S. al Fine

E -

Who's that you-der dressed in red?___ It must be the chil-dren that Mo - ses led.___

Every Mornin' When I Wake Up

PUPIL'S PAGE 275

Words and Music by Avon Gillespie
Piano Accompaniment by Bill and Pat Medley

Ev - er - y morn - in' when I wake up I have a new song to sing, my chil - dren, Ev - er - y morn - in'

when I wake up I have a new song to sing.

Fortune Favors the Brave

PUPIL'S PAGE 316

Music by Elton John
Words by Tim Rice
Piano Accompaniment by Dean Crocker

brave._____
(Oh.)_____

For - tune fa - vors___ the brave! We have swept to glo - ry.

E - gypt's mas - ter - y_____ ex - pands.___ From the Nile's___

north-ern del - ta to the dry, dry south-ern sands.___ The

more we find,___ the more we see,___ the more we come to learn.___

___ The more___ that we ex - plore,___ the

more we shall re - turn._____ Oh._____

For - tune fa - vors_____ the brave!_

The For - tune fa - vors_____ the

free. _____ For - tune
(Oh.) _____

fa - vors ____ the young. _____
(Oh.) _____

For - tune fa - vors ____ the brave! ____

Gee, Mom, I Want to Go Home

PUPIL'S PAGE 148

Traditional Army Song
Adapted by Oscar Brand
Arranged by Douglas Townsend
Piano Accompaniment by Larry Moore

150

The Ghost Ship

PUPIL'S PAGE 323

Words and Music by Don Besig and Nancy Price

Vocals begin on second repeat

1. Now

lis - ten well as a tale I tell of a
(2.) then I spied off the star - board side a____

night I shook with fear._____ We were
strange, mys - ter - ious sight._____ I____

strained   to   see   what the   sound   could   be,   some - thing
all   a - round   came a   mourn - ful   sound,   but I

flashed   and caught___ my   eye._____   And the
saw   not a   liv - ing   soul!_____

cold wind blew,_____

and the cold wind

blew._____ 2. 'Twas _____
_____ and the cold wind

And the cold wind blew._____ Well, I held fast to the for-ward

blew._____ Well, I held fast to the for-ward

mast as the ship moved slow - ly on,_____ And I

Fm   C

watched that way 'til the break of day, when I

Fm   B♭

knew that it fi - n'lly had gone._____ Oh, they laughed and

D♭   E♭   Fm   A♭

joked as I told my tale to the cap - tain and the men.____

Unison

____ But the sto - ry's true, I can prom - ise you, and it's

sure to hap-pen a - gain.____ Yes, it's sure____ to

hap - pen a - gain.____ And the

cold wind blew,_____

and the cold wind blew!_____

Git Along, Little Dogies

PUPIL'S PAGE 284

American Cowboy Song
Piano Accompaniment by Linda Worsley

as   he ap - proached he   was   sing - ing   this   song.
throw   the   do - gies out   on - to   the   trail. } Whoop-ee
know   that Wy - o - ming   will   be   your   new   home.

C   F   G7   C

ti - yi - yo,   git a - long   lit - tle   do - gies.   It's

B♭   Gm7   C7   F

your   mis - for - tune and   none   of   my   own;   Whoop-ee ti - yi - yo   git a-

B♭   Gm7   C7   F   C   F

long lit - tle   do - gies. You   know   that Wy - o - ming   will   be   your new home.

G7   C   C   F   G7   C

Gonna Build a Mountain

PUPIL'S PAGE 4

Words and Music by
Leslie Bricusse and Anthony Newley
Piano Accompaniment by Larry Moore

*Feet apart, rock side to side
slapping thighs on the beat*

Gon-na build a moun-tain from a lit-tle hill.
day-dream from a lit-tle hope.

Gon-na build a moun-tain, least I hope I will.
Gon-na push that day-dream up the moun-tain slope.

Stop   *Point R hand low to high*   *Shimmy R jazz hand high*

Gon-na build a moun-tain, gon-na build it high.
Gon-na build a day-dream, gon-na see it through.

Goober Peas

PUPIL'S PAGE 269

Civil War Marching Song
Piano Accompaniment by Larry Moore

1. Sit - ting by the road - side on a sum - mer day,
2. Just be - fore the bat - tle the Gen - 'ral hears a row,_____ He
3. Now our song has last - ed al - most long e - nough,_____ The

Chat - ting with my mess - mates, pass - ing time a - way.
says, "The Yanks are com - ing, I hear their ri - fles now!"_____ He
sub - ject's in - ter - est - ing, but rhymes are might - y rough.

Ly - ing in the shad - ow un - der - neath the trees,
turns a - round in won - der and what d'you think he sees?_____ The
When the war is o - ver, then free from rags and fleas,_____ We'll

Good - ness how de - li - cious! Eat - ing goo - ber peas!
Ten - nes - see Mi - li - tia eat - ing goo - ber peas!
kiss our wives and sweet - hearts and gob - ble goo - ber peas!

Refrain

Peas, peas, peas, peas, Eat - ing goo - ber peas!

Good - ness, how de - li - cious! Eat - ing goo - ber peas!

Good News

PUPIL'S PAGE 242

African American Spiritual
Piano Accompaniment by Marilyn Christensen

The Greenland Whale Fishery

PUPIL'S PAGE 212

English Sea Chantey
Piano Accompaniment by Larry Moore

The Guitar Man

PUPIL'S PAGE 138

Words and Music by Audrey Snyder
Piano Accompaniment by Larry Moore

Introduction not on Pupil's page

* *2nd time, 8-measure canon*

He sits and strums____ his gui-tar,____
His mag - ic fin - gers touch the strings.____

and weaves his thoughts in - to the mu - sic that he plays.____
The in - stru - ment be - gins to sing____ a

Peo - ple gath - er 'round,____ to hear the mag - ic sound.____ He
sim - ple mel - o - dy____ with six string har - mo - ny____ to

sings a tune - ful bal - lad from the heart.____ } And ev - 'ry-one
share the feel - ing words can nev - er bring.____

Interlude not shown in accompaniment

166

Hae Wa Be
(Sun and Rain)

PUPIL'S PAGE 273

Korean Children's Song
Collected and Transcribed by Kathy B. Sorensen
Piano Accompaniment by Larry Moore

Hava Nashira
(Sing Alleluia)

PUPIL'S PAGE 67

Music by Johannes Ockeghem
Traditional Words
Piano Accompaniment by Larry Moore

169

Heart

PUPIL'S PAGE 166

Words and Music by Richard Adler and Jerry Ross
Piano Accompaniment by Larry Moore

Relaxed Swing

You've got-ta have heart; All you real-ly need is heart. When the odds are say-in' you'll nev-er win, ____ That's when the grin ____ should start. You've got-ta have hope, Must-n't sit a-round and mope. Noth-in's half as bad as it may ap-pear; ____ Wait - 'll next year ____ and hope. When your luck is bat-tin'

170

Hotaru Koi
(Come, Firefly)

PUPIL'S PAGE 255

Japanese Folk Song
English Version by MMH
Piano Accompaniment by Bill and Pat Medley

Pronunciation: ho ho ho ta ru koi
English: **Ho!** **Ho!** **Fire - fly, please come!**

at chi no mi zu wa ni ga i zo.
You will find the wa - ter bad o - ver_____ there.

kot chi no mi zu wa a ma i zo.
All of the wa - ter's good here, near to me!

Huainito

PUPIL'S PAGE 351

Argentinian Folk Song
Arranged by Victoria Ebel-Sabo
Piano Accompaniment by Larry Moore

Spanish: Dos pa - lo - mi - tas se la - men - ta - ban llo - ran - do;

English: Two lit - tle doves were sit - ting to - geth - er, cry - ing so;

Dos — pa - lo - mi - tas se la - men - ta - ban, ah,_____ llo - ran - do;—

Two — lit - tle doves were sit - ting to - geth - er, ah,_____ cry - ing so;—

Y la u-na a la o-tra   se con-so-la-ban   di – cien – do:
One to the oth-er   in con-so-la-tion   mur – mured   low:

Y la u-na a la o-tra   se__con-so-la-ban, ah,_____   di – cien – do:
One to the oth-er   in con-so-la-tion, ah,_____   mur-mured low:__

¿Quien te ha cor-ta-do   tus be-llas a-las   pa – lo – ma?_____
Who could it be who's   tak-en your soft wings,   lit – tle   dove?_____

¿Quien te ha cor-ta   do tus__be-llas a-las,   ah,_____   pa-lo-ma?
Who__could it be   who's tak-en your soft   wings,   ah,_____   lit-tle dove?

¿Q_al-gun fal - sa - rio ha sor - pren - di - do tu vue - lo?
Who is the false one who took ad - van - tage of your love?

¿Q_al-gun fal - sa - rio ha__ sor - pren - di - do, ah,_____ tu vue - lo?___
Who is the false one who__ took ad - van - tage, ah,_____ of your love?___

Ah, ah, ah, pa - lo - ma,
Ah, ah, ah, lit - tle dove,

Ah,_____ ah,_____ pa - lo - ma,
Ah,_____ a,_____ lit - tle dove,

¿Q_al-gun fal-sa-rio ha sor-pren-di-do tu vue-lo?
Who is the false one who took ad-van-tage of your love?

¿Q_al-gun fal-sa-rio ha sor-pren-di-do ah,_____ tu vue-lo?__
Who is the false one who_ took ad-van-tage, ah,_____ of your love?__

Qui-so_el in-gra-to que yo mis a-las le die-ra,_____
It was a vil-lain to whom I gave my wings one day.__

Qui-so_el in-gra-to que_ yo mis a-las, ah,_____ le die-ra,__
It_ was a vil-lain to_whom I gave my, ah,_____ wings one day.__

Pa-ra_ir vo -lan - do   los dos jun - ti - tos   al   cie - lo.
He need-ed wings so   we could to -geth -er   fly   a - way.

Pa-ra_ir vo -lan - do   los__ dos jun - ti - tos, ah,_____   al cie - lo.__
He need-ed wings so   we__ could to -geth - er ah,_____   fly a - way.__

Por su ca - ri -ño   le di mis a - las   y   lue - go,_____
Sweet were his words, so   I gave my wings that   he   might   fly._____

Por__ su ca - ri -ño   le di mis a - las   ah,_____   y lue - go,__
Sweet__ were his words, so   I__ gave my wings that,   ah,_____   he might fly.__

A - ban-do - na - da   de de - sen - ga - ño   me   mue - ro.
When he'd de-ceived me,   he left me help-less   here   to   die.

A - ban-do - na - da   de de - sen - ga - ño, ah,————— me mue - ro.
When he'd de-ceived me,   he— left me help - less, ah,————— here to die.—

Ah,   ah,   ah,   y   lue - go
Ah,   ah,   ah,   sweet   his   words.

Ah,——————————— ah,——————————— y lue - go.
Ah,——————————— ah,——————————— sweet his words.

A - ban - do - na - da   de de - sen - ga - ño   me   mue -   ro.
When he'd de - ceived me,   he left me help - less   here   to   die.

A - ban - do - na - da   de de - sen - ga - ño, ah,_____   me mue - ro._____
When he'd de - ceived me,   he left me help - less ah,_____   here to die._____

Hullaballo Balay

PUPIL'S PAGE 10

English Sea Chantey
Piano Accompaniment by Larry Moore

Introduction not on Pupil's page

182

I Got a Letter

PUPIL'S PAGE 270

South Carolina Singing Game
Piano Accompaniment by Ian Williams

Solo
1. I got a let-ter this morn - ing,
2. I wrote a let-ter this morn - ing,
3. I mailed a let-ter this morn - ing,
Group
Oh, yes;

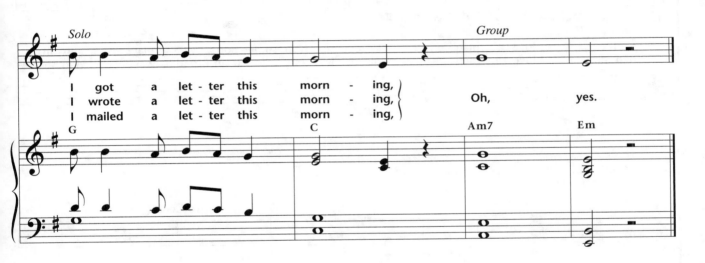

Solo
I got a let-ter this morn - ing,
I wrote a let-ter this morn - ing,
I mailed a let-ter this morn - ing,
Group
Oh, yes.

I Love a Piano

PUPIL'S PAGE 130

Words and Music by Irving Berlin
Piano Accompaniment by Larry Moore

I Want to Be Ready

PUPIL'S PAGE 12

African American Spiritual
Piano Accompaniment by Larry Moore

Introduction not on Pupil's page

Refrain

I want to be read - y, I want to be read - y,

I want to be read - y, to walk in Je - ru - sa - lem jus' like John.

Verse

1. Oh, John, oh, John, what do you say? To
2. John said the ci - ty was just four - square.

I'm Going to Georgia

PUPIL'S PAGE 244

North Carolina Folk Song
Piano Accompaniment by Larry Moore

I'm Gonna Sit at the Welcome Table

PUPIL'S PAGE 416

African American Spiritual
Piano Accompaniment by Larry Moore

189

If I Had a Hammer

PUPIL'S PAGE 174

Words and Music by Lee Hays and Pete Seeger
Arranged by Mary Goetze
Piano Accompaniment by Bill and Pat Medley

193

All _____ o - ver this land. _____

Ring, ring the bell. _____

Sing ah. _____

It Don't Mean a Thing

PUPIL'S PAGE 164

Words and Music by Duke Ellington and Irving Mills
Piano Accompaniment by Mark Brymer

It don't mean a thing, if it ain't got that swing, ___

(doo wah, ___ doo wah, doo wah, doo wah, doo wah, ___ doo wah, doo wah, doo

wah,) It don't mean a thing, ___ all you got to do is sing,

don't mean a thing, if it ain't got that swing,____ (doo wah,____ doo wah,

doo wah, doo wah, doo wah,____ doo wah, doo wah, doo wah.) It wah.)

Já do lesa nepojedu
(To the Woods I Will Not Go)

PUPIL'S PAGE 227

Czech Folk Song
Piano Accompaniment by Larry Moore

Introduction not on Pupil's page

Czech: Já do le - sa ne - po - je - du, já do le - sa ne - pu - du,

English: To the woods I will not go now, to the woods I will not go.

kdy - by na mě haj - ný při - šel, on by mi vzal se - ky - rú

If the ran - ger should come near me, he would take my ax a - way.

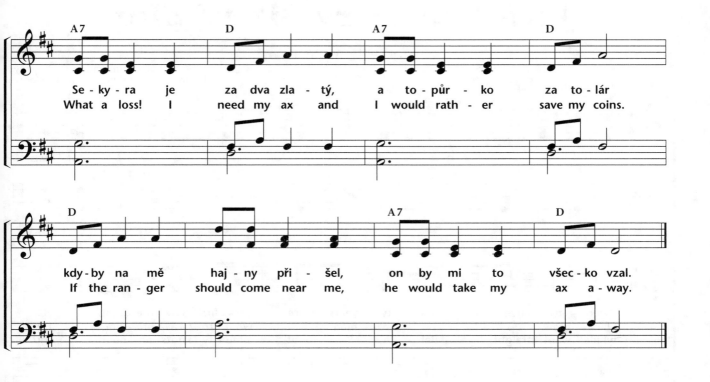

Se - ky - ra je za dva zla - tý, a to - půr - ko za to - lár
What a loss! I need my ax and I would rath - er save my coins.

kdy - by na mě haj - ny při - šel, on by mi to všec - ko vzal.
If the ran - ger should come near me, he would take my ax a - way.

Jack Was Ev'ry Bit a Sailor

PUPIL'S PAGE 170

Newfoundland Sea Chantey
Piano Accompaniment by Larry Moore

Introduction not on Pupil's page

twen - ty - five or thir - ty years since Jack first saw the light. He
Jack grew up to be a man, he went to La - bra - dor; He
whale went straight for Baf - fin's Bay 'bout nine - ty knots an hour. And

came in - to this world of woe one dark and storm - y night. He was
fished in In - dian Har - bor where his fa - ther fished be - fore; On
ev - 'ry time he'd blow a spray, he'd send it in a show-er. "Oh,

born on board his fa - ther's ship as she was ly - ing to, 'bout
his re - turn - ing in the fog he met a heav - y gale, And
now," says Jack un - to him - self, "I must see what he's a - bout." He

1. 'Twas

twen - ty five or thir - ty miles south - east of Bac - al - hao.
Jack was swept in - to the sea and swal - lowed by a whale.
caught the whale all by the tale and turned him in - side out.

Refrain

Jack was ev - 'ry bit a sail - or Five and twen - ty years a

wha - ler. Jack was ev - 'ry bit a sail - or. He was

1., 2.

born up - on the bright blue sea.

2. When sea.
3. The

Jede, jede, poštovský panáček
(Riding, Riding, Is Mr. Postman)

PUPIL'S PAGE 226

Introduction not on Pupil's page

Czech Folk Song
Piano Accompaniment by Larry Moore

Czech: Je - de, je - de, poš - tov - ský pa - ná - ček,
English: 1. Rid - ing, rid - ing, Post - Man is rid - ing

je - de, je - de poš - tov - ský pán,
rid - ing, rid - ing, is Mis - ter Post.

1. Vpře - du - má tru - bič - ku, vza - du má truh - lič - ku,
Blow - ing his horn, he calls, Bear - ing the trunk he hauls,
2. Má vra - ny ko - ni - ãky ja - ko dvů ry - bi - ãky,

je - de, je - de poš - tov - ský pán.
rid - ing rid - ing is Mis - ter Post.
je - de, je - de do Ro - ky - can.

202

Jikel' emaweni
(Throw It Down the Slope)

PUPIL'S PAGE 70

South African Work Song
Arranged by Cheryl Lavender
Piano Accompaniment by Larry Moore

Xhosa: Ji - kel' e - ma - we - ni ndi - ya - ham - ba.   Ji - kel' e - ma - we - ni ndi - ya-

ham - ba.   ham - ba.   A - jik' a - ma - do - da   a - ji - ke lem - go - di - ni A-

A - ji - kel' e - ma - we - ni.   A-

ji - kel'u Ra - de - be,   A - ji - kel'e ma - we - ni.   A - ji - kel'e ma - we - ni.

Sing 2nd time

ji - kel - a   e - ma - we - ni.   A   -   ni.

Am/D   G   G

Ⓐ

Ji - kel' e - ma - we - ni ndi - ya - ham - ba.   Ji - kel' e - ma - we - ni ndi - ya -

G   A   Am/D

ham - ba.   ham - ba.   A - jik' a - ma - do - da   a - ji - ke lem - go - di - ni A -

G   G   G   Am

ji - kel'u Ra - de - be,   A - ji - kel'e ma - we - ni.   A - ji - kel'e ma - we - ni.

Joban Tanko Bushi
(Joban Miner's Song)

PUPIL'S PAGE 142

Japanese Folk Song
Arranged by Wendy B. Stuart
Piano Accompaniment by Larry Moore

to 1. ha
2. ha

a sa mo ha yo ka ɾa
o ɾa ga ta ņ ko ni

yo
yo

ka ņ te ɾa
i chi do wa

sa ge te
go za ɾe

Chant:

nai
nai

ha yoi sho yoi sho yoi sho

ko na i ma wa ɾi mo yo
gi ɾi to ni ņ io no yo

don to nu shi   no ta me nai   ha yoi sho yoi sho yoi sho
kon to ha na   ga sa ku nai

to to to to to to to to to to to to to to to to

ha

a sa mo ha yo ka ra yo

to to to to to to   to to to to to to   to to to to

nai ha yoi sho yoi sho yoi sho to to to to to to to to

to to to to to

Vocables: cho chong ga chong

to to to to to to to to chong

cho chong ga chong ton

Jordan's Angels

PUPIL'S PAGE 365

Words and Music by Rollo A. Dilworth
Based on the Spiritual "All Night, All Day"
Piano Accompaniment by Larry Moore

an - gels   keep a - watch - in'   o - ver   me, _____ my Lord.

an - gels   keep a - watch - in'   o - ver me, o - ver me, ____ my Lord.

All _____ night,   all _____ day, _____

All _____ night and ____ all _____ day. _____

an - gels watch - in' o - ver me!

Some - day my soul shall be free. I shall be free.

Look-in' out o-ver Jor - dan, all I could see:

Look-in' out o-ver Jor-dan, all I could see was a

a band of an-gels that were com-in'_____ af-ter me.

band, a band of an-gels that were com-in' af-ter me.

Ga-bri-el was on the trum-pet and Dav-id was play-in' the

Ga-bri-el was play-in' the trum-pet. Dav-id was play-in' the

cresc.

harp.____ Some - day my soul____ shall be free!____

harp.____ Some - day my soul shall be free!____

Look-in' out o-ver Jor-dan, all I could see was a band of an - gels com-in' for me!

Look-in' out o-ver Jor-dan, all I could see was a band of an - gels com-in' for me!

All night, all day, an-gels keep watch - in' me, my Lord!

Look-in' out o-ver Jor-dan, all I could see was a band of an - gels com-in' for me!

sub. mp ... *poco rit.*

An - gels, an - gels. I shall be free!

An - gels, an - gels. I shall be free!

Kakokolo

PUPIL'S PAGE 262

Words and Music by Samite
Piano Accompaniment by Bill and Pat Medley

Luganda: Ka - ko - ko - lo gwe ka - ko - ko - lo,_____

English: Ka - ko - ko - lo, Hey! ka - ko - ko - lo,_____

Ka - ko - ko - lo kwa - ta en - ton - go - li yo._____

Ka - ko - ko - lo Oh,___ take up your gui - tar!_____

N - de - ter - a, maa - ma, nde - ter - a. A gen - da - no___ mu - lun -

Bring it to me, ma - ma, play a song. Don't tell me___ you are

Repeat refrain last time only

Kokoleoko

PUPIL'S PAGE 279

Liberian Folk Song
Piano Accompaniment by Bill and Pat Medley

220

La Bamba

PUPIL'S PAGE 381

Traditional Mexican Folk Song
Adaped and arranged by Roger Emerson
Piano Accompaniment by Larry Moore

gra-cia. Un-a po-ca de gra - cia para mi, para ti._____ y a-rri-ba y_a-rri-

_ba, y_a-rri - ba, y_a-rri - ba por ti se-re'_____ por ti se-re'_____ por ti se-re'.

Bam - ba, bam - ba. Bam - ba, bam - ba. Bam - ba.

Pa - ra bai-lar La Bam - ba, pa - ra bai-lar La Bam - ba, se ne-ce - si -

224

ta u-na po-ca de gra-cia.   Un-a po-ca de gra - cia para mi, para ti,—

D.S. al Coda

—— y a-rri-ba y a-rri - ba,

226

La pájara pinta
(The Speckled Bird)

PUPIL'S PAGE 268

Mexican Folk Song
Piano Accompaniment by Carol Jay

Introduction not in Pupil's Edition

Spanish: Y_es - ta - ba la pá - ja - ra pin - ta sen -
English: A bright speck-led bird___ was sit - ting up -

ta - da_en su ver - de li - món.___ Con el pi - co re - co - ge las
on a green lem - on branch.___ With her beak___ she gath - ered

flo - res, Con el pi - co re - co - ge_el a - mor. Ay, ay, ay,
flow - ers, with her beak___ she gath - ered love, Ay, ay, ay,

227

ay!_____ ¿En dón-de la en-cuen-tro yo?_____ Con el pi-co re-co-ge las
ay!_____ Then tell me where will it be?_____ With her beak____ she gath - ered

flo - res, Con el pi-co re-co-ge el a - mor._____
flow - ers, with her beak____ she gath - ered love._____

Lean on Me

PUPIL'S PAGE 150

Words and Music by Bill Withers
Piano Accompaniment by Bill and Pat Medley

1. Some - times in our lives ___ we all have pain ___ we all have sor -
2. Please swal - low your pride ___ if I have things ___ you need to bor -

- row. ___ But if we are wise ___ we know that there's ___
row ___ for no one can fill ___ those of your needs ___

___ al - ways to - mor - row. ___ } Lean on me when you're not strong ___
___ that you won't let ___ show. ___

and I'll be your friend_____ I'll help you car - ry on_____

for it won't be long_____ 'til I'm gon-na need_____ some-bod-y to lean_____

1.
_____ on._____

2.
_____ on._____ You just call on me, broth - er, when

you need a hand,_____ we all need some-bod-y to lean_____ on._____ I just

on.____ You just ____ if you just call_____ me.____

G   C   G7   C   G7   C

Leila

PUPIL'S PAGE 376

Folk Song from North Carolina
Arranged by MMH

234

Les anges dans nos campagnes
(Angels We Have Heard on High)

PUPIL'S PAGE 406

French Carol
Piano Accompaniment by Larry Moore

Allegretto

Verse

French: Les an - ges dans___ nos cam - pa - gnes out en - ton - né l'hym - ne des cieux,

English: 1. An - gels we have___ heard on high,___ Sweet - ly___ sing - ing___ o're the plains,

2. Shep - herds why this___ ju - bi - lee?___ Why your___ joy - ous___ strains pro - long?

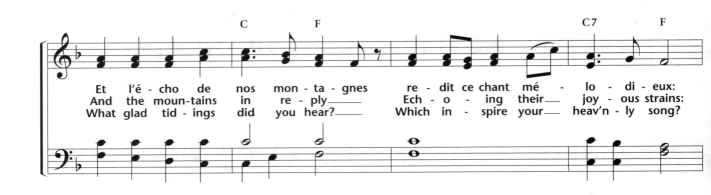

Et l'é-cho de nos mon-ta-gnes re-dit ce chant mé - lo - di-eux:
And the moun-tains in re-ply___ Ech - o - ing their___ joy - ous strains:
What glad tid - ings did you hear?___ Which in - spire your___ heav'n - ly song?

Refrain
descant

Glo - - - ri a in ex-cel-sis De - o,

Glo - - - ri - a in ex - cel - sis De - o,

Glo - - ri - a in ex-cel-sis De - o.

Glo - - - ri - a in ex - cel - sis De - o.

Let It Roll

PUPIL'S PAGE 124

Words and Music by Paul Kennerley
Piano Accompaniment by Larry Moore

Let Music Surround You

PUPIL'S PAGE 285

Words and Music by Fran Addicott
Piano Accompaniment by Carol Jay

Let mu-sic sur-round you. Let it fill your heart.

Those who sing in har-mon-y____ nev-er grow a-part.

Listen to the Music

PUPIL'S PAGE 63

Words and Music by Ed Robertson

Pupil book repeats

242

mu - sic. Let it speak to you.

Won't you lis-ten to the mu - sic: Let it speak to you.

sing - ing. Lis-ten to the mu - sic ring: Let it speak to you.

C/G G C/D D G

rit.

you.

rit.

you.

rit.

you.

G C G D7 D G

rit.

Lonesome Dove

PUPIL'S PAGE 249

Tennessee Folk Song
Piano Accompaniment by Larry Moore

1. Down in some lone - some, pin - ey grove,
2. I once, like you, I had a mate,

Down in some lone - some, pin - ey grove,
I once, like you, I had a mate,

My lit - tle dove, she sits and moans.
But now, like you, I'm des - o - late.

244

Lullaby of Broadway

PUPIL'S PAGE 182

Words and Music by Al Dubin and Harry Warren
Piano Accompaniment by Larry Moore

Relaxed Swing

Introduction not on Pupil's page

Reach both hands to audience

Jazz hands at shoulder height, sway L R

Shimmy jazz hands at head level

1. Come on a-long and lis-ten to— The lull-a-by of Broad-way.
2. Come on a-long an lis-ten to— The lull-a-by of Broad-way.

Salute

Reach R jazz hand high

Jazz hands at shoulder level, sway L R

Shimmy jazz hands at head level

The hip hoo-ray and bal-ly - hoo,— The lull-a-by of Broad-way.
The hi-dee-hi and boop-a - doo,— The lull-a-by of Broad-way.

v1: Face stage R with R hand up as though holding a subway strap. Bounce on your heels to show motion

v1: Face front, bounce a bit more as though you are on a wild cab ride

v2: Pretend to play a trumpet

The rum-ble of a sub-way train,— The rat-tle of the tax - is,—
The band be-gins to go to town,— And ev-'ry-one goes cra - zy.

246

The Lumber Camp Song

PUPIL'S PAGE 136

Canadian Folk Song
Piano Accompaniment by Larry Moore

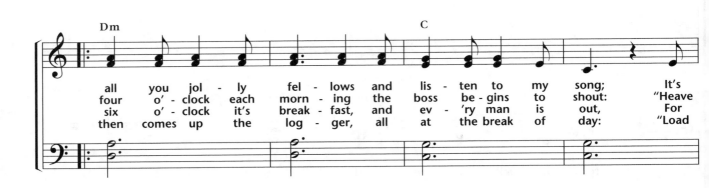

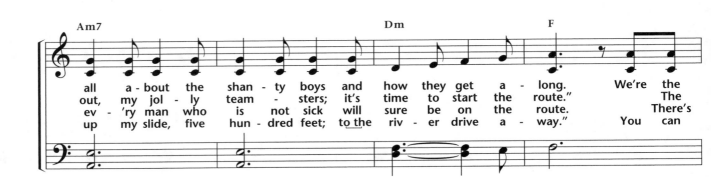

248

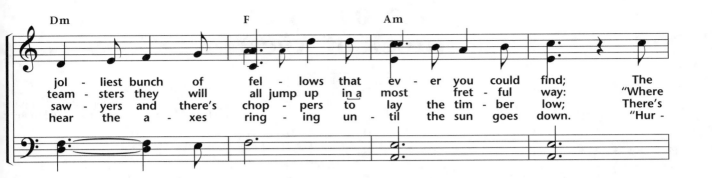

jol - liest bunch of fel - lows that ev - er you could find; The
team - sters they will all jump up in a most fret - ful way: "Where
saw - yers and there's chop - pers to lay the tim - ber low; There's
hear the a - xes ring - ing un - til the sun goes down. "Hur -

way we spend our win - ter months is hurl - ing down the pine. 2. At
is me boots? Where is me pants? Me socks is gone as - tray!" 3. At
swam - pers and there's log - gers to drag it to and fro. 4. And
rah, my boys! The day is spent. To the shan - ty we are

bound."
At
At
And

Ma'oz Tsur
(Rock of Ages)

PUPIL'S PAGE 405

Jewish Folk Song
Piano Accompaniment by Larry Moore

Introduction not on Pupil's page

ma oz tsur yε shu a ti lε xa na e lε sha be ax
Rock of ag - es, all our days, We fill the air with_____ songs of praise.

ti kon beit tε fi la ti vε sham to da nε za be ax lε
All our foes thou will as - sail. Thy strength and pow - er_____ will not fail. We'll

et ta xin mat be ax, mi tsar ha na be ax
de - di-cate the al - tar, Faith will nev - er fal - ter.

az eg moɾ bɛ shir miz moɾ xa nu kat ha miz be ax be ax
With our house of prayer re-stored, Fill the air with___ hymns of praise. hymns of praise.

Mama Don't 'Low

PUPIL'S PAGE 126

American Folk Song
Piano Accompaniment by Larry Moore

1.
2. } Ma - ma don't 'low no { gui - tar play - in' round here, ____
3. } { ban - jo pick - in' round here, ____
{ har - mo - niz - in' round here, ____

Ma - ma don't 'low no { gui - tar play - in' round here, ____
{ ban - jo pick - in' round here, ____
{ har - mo - niz - in' round here, ____

I don't care what Ma-ma don't 'low, Gon-na { play my gui-tar an-y-how,
pick my ban-jo an-y-how,
har-mon-ize my songs an-y-how,

Ma-ma don't 'low no { gui-tar play-in' round here._____
ban-jo pick-in' round here._____
har-mo-niz-in' round here._____

Mama Will Provide

Music by Stephen Flaherty
Words by Lynn Ahrens
Piano Accompaniment by Larry Moore

256

Mayim, Mayim
(Water, Water)

PUPIL'S PAGE 102

Words and Music by E. Amiran
Arranged by Valerie Shields
Piano Accompaniment by Larry Moore

Mele Kalikimaka
(Merry Christmas)

PUPIL'S PAGE 410

Brightly

Introduction not on Pupil's page

Words and Music by R. Alex Anderson
Piano Accompaniment by Larry Moore

Me - le Ka - li - ki - ma - ka is the thing to say, ____ on a

bright Ha - wai - ian Christ-mas day, ____ That's the is - land

greet - ing that we send to you, ____ from the land where palm trees

sway._____ Here we know that Christ-mas will be green and

bright, the sun will shine by day, and all the stars at night,

Me - le Ka - li - ki - ma - ka is Ha - wai - i's way to

say Mer - ry Christ-mas to you._____ you._____

Merecumbé

PUPIL'S PAGE 276

Puerto Rican Children's Game Song
Arranged by Alejandro Jimenez
English Words by Linda Worsley
Piano Accompaniment by Larry Moore

Introduction not on Pupil's page

Spanish: El Juez le di-jo al
English: The judge said to the

cu-ra. El cu-ra le di-jo al juez. A dón-de es-tá ese rit-mo, ca-ram-ba
pa-dre, The pa-dre said to the judge, Where did we get this rhy-thm, *ca-ram-ba?*

del me-re-cum-bé, ¡eh! Che qui mo-re-na, che qui. Che qui mo-re-na, ¡eh! A-
The *me-re-cum-bé,* eh! *Che qui mo-re-na, che qui!* *Che qui mo-re-na,* eh! You

dón-de es-tá ese rit-mo ca-ram-ba del me-re-cum-bé.
can't re-sist the rhy-thm, *ca-ram-ba!* This *Me-re-cum-bé!*

Un pa - si - to pa - ra a'-lan - te, un pa - si - to pa - ra a - trás,
Take a step, a small step for - ward, Take a step, a small step back - ward,

dan - do que dan - do la me - dia vuel - ta, ¿quién se que - da - rá? ¡eh!
Now turn a lit - tle, a half turn 'round, Now you know how it's done! eh!

Mi caballo blanco
(My White Horse)

PUPIL'S PAGE 60

Words and Music by Francisco Flores del Campo
English Words by Linda Worsley
Piano Accompaniment by Larry Moore

Spanish: Es mi ca-ba-llo blan-co___ Co-mo_un a-ma-ne-cer
English: 1. This is my trus-ty white horse,___ I love him like a friend,
2. On wings of my good for-tune,___ he took me ev-'ry day,
3. When I am called to hea-ven,___ the an-gels have to know.

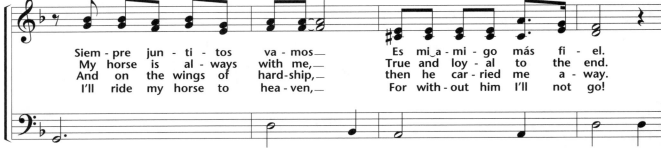

Siem-pre jun-ti-tos va-mos___ Es mi_a-mi-go más fi-el.
My horse is al-ways with me,___ True and loy-al to the end.
And on the wings of hard-ship,___ then he car-ried me a-way.
I'll ride my horse to hea-ven,___ For with-out him I'll not go!

Refrain

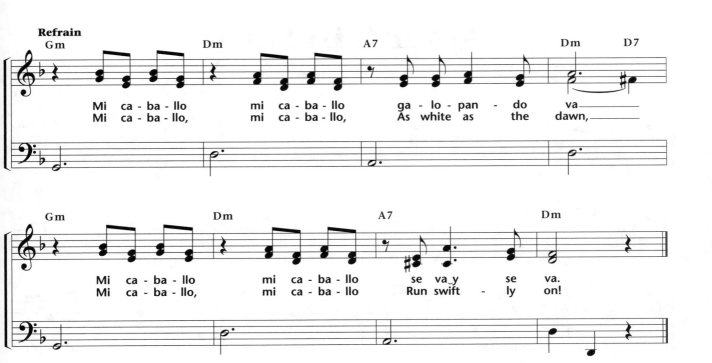

Mi ca - ba - llo   mi ca - ba - llo   ga - lo - pan - do   va
Mi ca - ba - llo,   mi ca - ba - llo,   As white as   the   dawn,

Mi ca - ba - llo   mi ca - ba - llo   se va y   se va.
Mi ca - ba - llo,   mi ca - ba - llo   Run swift - ly   on!

Mountain Music

PUPIL'S PAGE 20

Words and Music by Randy Owen
Piano Accompaniment by Larry Moore

270

On the verses, make a family portrait and bounce along to the beat. could add some washboards, jugs, washtub basses, etc.

2. Climb - ing tall hick' - ry
back-home___ come on mu - sic
like Tom Saw - yer
That comes___
Ride a raft_____
bend - ing o - ver_____
like old__ Huck
skin - nin'
from the

Finn,___
cats,___
heart,___
Take a nap_____
Play - in' base - ball_____
Play some thing_____
like Rip__ Van
with
with lots__ of

Wink - le
chert__ rocks
feel - ing
Daze dream - ing_____ a - gain.
us-ing saw - mill slabs__ for bats.
'cause that's where mu - sic has__ to__ start.
Oh

D.S. al Fine

271

Mr. Scott Joplin's Ragtime Rag

PUPIL'S PAGE 110

Words by Mark Brymer
Music by Scott Joplin
Piano Accompaniment by Larry Moore

Never Sleep Late Anymore

PUPIL'S PAGE 274

American Folk Song
Piano Accompaniment by Larry Moore

Neviděli jste tu mé panenky?
(Have You Not Seen My Daughters?)

PUPIL'S PAGE 228

Czech Folk Song
Piano Accompaniment by Larry Moore

Czech: Ne - vi - dě - li jste tu mé pa - nen - ky? šla do le - sa na ma - len - ky,
English: Oh, have you not seen my dear-est daugh-ters? to the woods they went for ber - ries.

ne - vi - dě - li jste tu mé pa - nen - ky, šla do le - sa trá - vu žit;
Oh, have you not seen my dear-est daugh-ters cut-ting grass up to the woods?

šla do le - sa, by - la ro - sa, zá - blo ju to, by - la ro - sa,
When they left home, it was morn - ing; bare-foot roam - ers, I am mourn - ing.

275

The New Ashmolean Marching Society and Students Conservatory Band

PUPIL'S PAGE 308

Words and Music by Frank Loesser
Piano Accompaniment by Dean Crocker

1. Here they come with the sun - light on the trum - pets.
march on - ly slight - ly out of tem - po,

Here they come with the ban - ners fly - ing high.
though they play just a tri - fle out of tune,

In my throat I've a lump-y sort of feel-ing
though there's just a sug - ges - tion in the o - boe

and the bright gleam of pride is in my eye.
of the sound of a hound be - neath the moon;

Here they come with the clar - i - nets a - wail-ing.
though the trom - bone's a lit - tle in - de - pen - dent,

Here they come rath - er brave - ly up the square.
and the drum - mer is not ex - act - ly choice,

And I know in a mo - ment I'll be cheer - ing
still the old col - lege spir - it is up - on me,

and my fine Sun - day hat will be high in the
and I shout ev - 'ry time at the top of my

air ... for ... The ... New ... New ... Ash ... - ... mo ... - ... le - an ... March - ing ... So -
voice ... for ... The ... New ... New ... Ash ... - ... mo ... - ... le - an ... March - ing ... So -

ci ... - ... e - ty ... and ... Stu - dents ... Con ... - ... serv ... - ... a - to - ry ... Band.
ci ... - ... e - ty ... and ... Stu - dents ... Con ... - ... serv ... - ... a - to - ry

2. Though they ... Band.

Yes, The New Ash - mo - le-an March-ing So - ci - e - ty and

Stu - dents Con - serv - a - to - ry Band.

Night of Stars/Silent Night

PUPIL'S PAGE 412

"Night of Stars" Words and Music by Linda Worsley
"Silent Night" Words by Josef Mohr, Music by Franz Grüber

Part 1 and Part 2

Unison

Night of won-der, night of stars, one bright-er star a-bove.

Lis-ten now to an-gels sing-ing. Hear the joy-ful mes-sage ring-ing:

Peace, peace, to all ___ man-kind. Hope and love and peace. Night of

stars, night of peace. Night of hope and love and peace.

Part 2

Si - lent night, ho - ly night. All is calm,

all is bright 'round yon vir - gin moth - er and child. Ho - ly in-fant so

ten - der and mild. Sleep in heav - en - ly peace,_____ Sleep___ in heav - en - ly

Part 1

Night of won - der, night of stars,

Part 2

peace._____ Si - lent night, ho - ly night.

one bright - er star a - bove. Lis - ten now to an - gels sing - ing.

All is calm, all is bright 'round yon vir - gin moth - er and child.

Hear the joy - ful mes - sage ring - ing; Peace, peace, to all__ man - kind.

Ho - ly in - fant so ten - der and mild. Sleep in heav - en - ly peace,__

Hope and love and peace. Night of stars, night of peace. Night of

Sleep__ in heav - en - ly peace.__ Sleep in heav - en - ly peace,__

hope and love and peace.__ Peace.__

Sleep__ in heav - en - ly peace.__ Peace.__

N'kosi sikelel' iAfrika
(Lord Bless Africa)

PUPIL'S PAGE 339

Words and Music by E. M. Sontonga
Piano Accompaniment by Cheryl Lavender

287

Ku - de ku - be ngu - na pha - ka - de, Ku - de ku - be ngu - na pha - ka - de!

Ku - de ku - be ngu - na pha - ka - de, Ku - de ku - be ngu - na pha - ka - de!

Ku - de ku - be ngu - na pha - ka - de, Ku - de ku - be ngu - na pha - ka - de!

O, Desayo

PUPIL'S PAGE 50

Angolan Folk Song
Arranged by Elliot Z. Levine
English Words by Elliot Z. Levine
Piano Accompaniment by Mark Brymer

Refrain

Portuguese: O, Des - ay - o! O, Des - ay - o!

O, Des - ay - o Me - ni - na, O, Des - ay - o!

Verse 1

Part I

Rains are o - ver, it's fine and shin - y wea-ther O, Des - ay - o!

C   F   C   F

Part II

Fine and shin - y day for a get__ to - ge-ther, O, Des - ay - o!

C   F   C   F

Verse 2

Part I

O, Des - ay - o,_____ Me - ni - na.   O, Des - ay - o,_____ Me - ni - na,

Part II

Sing,   a song___ and then   dance a - long___ and then,

C   F

O, Des - ay - o,___ Me - ni - na   O, Des - ay - o,___ Me - ni - na   Off they go___ and good -

drink a cup___ and then   stay   for sup - per then.   Off we go___ a - gain

bye,   we've got   to say___ good - bye!

down the stream___ a - gain   off we go___ a - gain   down the stream___ a - gain.

O La Le!

PUPIL'S PAGE 6

Words and Music by Hugh A. Davis
Piano Accompaniment by Mark Brymer

Interludes in Pupil Edition do not appear

Al - le, al - le, al - le - lu - u - ia.

Al - le, al - le, al - le - lu - u - ia.

F   B♭   C   F

O_____ sing la la.   O_____ sing la la.

O_____   la la O_____   la la

F   C7   F   B♭6   C7   Dm   C   F

Oh, How Lovely Is the Evening

PUPIL'S PAGE 252

English Round
Piano Accompaniment by Bill and Pat Medley

Oh, how love - ly is the eve - ning, is the eve - ning,

When the bells are sweet - ly ring - ing, sweet - ly ring - ing,

Ding, dong, ding, dong, ding, dong.

The Old Barn Dance

PUPIL'S PAGE 94

Words and Music by Jan Reese
Piano Accompaniment by Mark Brymer

298

Coda

Patty cake
Slap legs   *Clap*   *High 10*   *Clap*

read - y   for   some   fun   at   the   Old   Barn   Dance!   Get

Swing lasso overhead with R hand   *Pat legs* *Clap* *Present high*

read - y for some fun_____   at   the   Old   Barn   Dance!"

Old Jim John

PUPIL'S PAGE 253

American Folk Song
Piano Accompaniment by Mark Brymer

Old Jim John, he's the old-est man to sit up-on the seat by yon-der___ sy-ca-more tree. Old Jim John, when he is dead and gone, there'll be none left on as___ old as he.

Ole La'u Papa e

PUPIL'S PAGE 91

Tongan Stick Game Song
Collected and Transcribed by Kathy B. Sorensen
Piano Accompaniment by Bill and Pat Medley

On a Clear Day

PUPIL'S PAGE 206

Words by Alan Jay Lerner
Music by Burton Lane
Piano Accompaniment by Mark Brymer

304

glow of your be - ing Out - shines ev -'ry star. You feel part of

Bm7   B♭dim   Am7   Dm7

_ Ev -'ry moun-tain, sea and shore._____ You can hear from far and

Dm7   G7   Dm7   CM7   Bm7

near a world you've nev - er heard be - fore._____ And on a clear day,_____

A7   Am7   Gdim   GM7

One Dime Blues

PUPIL'S PAGE 178

Words and Music by Blind Lemon Jefferson
Piano Accompaniment by Mark Brymer

ain't_____ got a dime._____
Cair - o street one day,_____
all_____ that I had._____

Ev - 'ry -
One____
Got a

D7

D.S.

bod - y gets in hard___ luck some - time.
dime_____ was all___ that I had.
meal_____ be - fore the last._____

A7

G7

D7

One of Those Songs

PUPIL'S PAGE 54

English Words by Will Holt
Music by Gerald Calvi
Piano Accompaniment by Mark Brymer

Vaudeville rocks

L R L R L R L R

one of those songs——— that you hear for a while,——— that The
eve - ning you part - ed, the morn - ing you met,——— The You
on you'll re - call——— it in some oth - er year,——— You

F FM7 F FM7 F6 FM7 F FM7 F FM7

Clutch heart, lean L *Lean R*

come in - to fash - ion and go out of style,——— It's
love of your life——— you can nev - er for - get,——— The
may start to smile——— or you may shed a tear,——— You'll

F FM7 F D7(♭9) D7 Gm

Face L, point R hand at audience *Face R, point L hand at audience*

one of those songs——— that you think you for - got,———
rea - son is sim - ple, the mem - 'ry be - longs,———
find that one part——— of your life - time be - longs———

B♭/D B♭m6/D♭ F/C FM7/C D7

311

Orange Blossom Special

PUPIL'S PAGE 33

Train Starting (♩ = 80)

Introduction not on Pupil's page

Words and Music by Ervin T. Rouse
Piano Accompaniment by Mark Brymer

com - in' down that rail - road track! It's the Or - ange Blos - som
get some sand in — my shoes. I'll ride that Or - ange Blos - som
fast - est train on — the line. It's that Or - ange Blos - som

Spe - cial bring - in' my ba - by
Spe - cial and lose these New York
Spe - cial roll - in' down the Sea - board

1., 2.
back.
blues.

3.
line.

accel. e cresc.

accel. e cresc.

314

Our Goodman

PUPIL'S PAGE 245

Appalachian Folk Song
Piano Accompaniment by Mark Brymer

noth - ing but a milk cow my moth - er sent to me.
noth - ing but a cab-bage head my moth - er sent to me.
noth - ing but a dish - rag my moth - er sent to me.
noth - ing but a ba-by child my moth - er sent to me.
It's

G   C   D7   D7sus/A   G   Am7

miles   I have trav - eled, some for - ty miles or more,

A
A
A
A

G

milk   cow with   a   sad - dle   on   I   nev - er saw be - fore.
cab - bage head with boot heels on I nev - er saw be - fore.
dish - rag with a hat - band on I nev - er saw be - fore.
ba - by child with mous - tache on I nev - er saw be - fore.

G   C   D   D7   D7sus/A   G

Pauper sum ego
(I Am Poor)

PUPIL'S PAGE 254

Latin Canon
English Words by Linda Worsley
Piano Accompaniment by Mark Brymer

Latin: Pau - per sum e - go. Ni - hil ha - be - o. Cor me - um da - bo.
English: Though I may be poor, noth-ing can I give, but my hum-ble heart.

Accompaniment for unison version

A Perfect Winter Day

PUPIL'S PAGE 400

Words and Music by Teresa and Paul Jennings
Piano Accompaniment by Mark Brymer

round me. I was a-slid-in'. My feet were glid-in'. It was a

head (sniff) cold. (sniff) I think it's cold and wet and mes-sy and slop-py. Just a

Gm   C7   F   B♭

per-fect win-ter day! What a per-fect day to

per-fect win-ter (sniff), if you like that sort of thing. I

Gm7   C7   F   B♭

build a snow-man! Build a snow-man! Build a snow-man!

have a head-ache. My eyes itch. My nose is

F   Gm   C7   F

What a per-fect day to build a snow-man! A per-fect win-ter

clogged. Oh, I feel crum-my on this per-fect win-ter

B♭   F   C7

1., 2.

2nd time only

day!   It was a -

Sniff, cough freely _

day.

1., 2.

F   D7   Gm   C7   F   D7   Gm

day!   What a per-fect day to build   a snow-man!   Build a snow-man!

day!   I   have   a head - ache.   My   eyes   itch.

Build   a snow-man!   What a per-fect day to   build   a snow-man!   A

My   nose   is   clogged.   Oh,   I   feel   crum - my on this

perfect winter day!

perfect winter day.

Yes, It's a perfect winter day!

Random gleeful sounds

Perfect winter day!

Group sneeze: Achoo!

Random sniffling, etc.

Pick a Bale of Cotton

PUPIL'S PAGE 254

African American Folk Song
Piano Accompaniment by Mark Brymer

Rage and Roar

PUPIL'S PAGE 48

Words and Music by Liz Gilpatrick
Piano Accompaniment by Mark Brymer

Harmonization for unison only

Red Iron Ore

PUPIL'S PAGE 134

Boat Song from the Great Lakes Region
Arranged by Michael Jothen
Piano Accompaniment by Mark Brymer

Introduction not on Pupil's page

1. Come
2. In the
3. Next
4. The
5.
6. In

all	ye	bold	sail - ors	that	fol -	low	the lake	On an
month	of	Sep -	tem - ber	that the	sev - en -	teenth	day,	Two___
morn - ing	we	hove	a - long -	side	the	*Ex -*	*ile.*	And___
tug	*Es* -	*can - a -*	*ba*	she	towed	out	the *Minch,*	The___
Through___	Louse	Is -	land	it	blew	a	fresh breeze;	Made the
Cleve -	land's	safe	har - bour	the	*Rob -*	*erts*	now firm.	Tis a

i - ron ore ves - sel your liv - ing to make. I
dol - lars and a quar - ter is all they would pay. And
soon was made fast to an i - ron ore pile, They
Rob - erts she thought she had left in a pinch And
Fox - es, the Bea - vers, the Skill - a - ge - les; We
big bit of boast - ing for which we all yearn! For

Cm   B♭   G

shipped in Chi - ca - go, Bid a - dieu to the shore, Bound a -
on Mon - day morn - ing the___ *Bridge - port* did take The___
low - er'd their chutes and like___ thun - der did roar, They___
as she passed by us, she bid us good - bye, Say - ing,
flew by the *Minch*___ for to show her the way, And she
ol' Cap - tain Shan - non had___ ought to stand treat, For___

Cm   Fm   B♭   E♭

way to Es - ca - na - ba for red i - ron ore.
ore ship, E. C. Rob - erts far out in the lake.
spout - ed in - to us that red i - ron ore.
"We'll meet you in Cleve - land next Fourth of Ju - ly!"
ne'er hove in＿ sight till we were off Thun - der Bay.
mak - ing here＿ safe - ly a - head of the fleet.

Sing after verses 3–6 only **Refrain**
Part II

Der - ry

Refrain
Part I

3.–6. D.C.

Down, down, down der - ry down.

down, down, down der - ry down.

Ride on the Wind

PUPIL'S PAGE 326

Words and Music by Mark Patterson
Piano Accompaniment by Larry Moore

heart set the course,—— set your spir-it free—— as you ride on the wind,——

the wind of your dreams. Ride on the wind,—— young sail-or,

ride up-on—— your—— dreams. Find your way—— on the o-pen sea,—— then

26
set the course, set your spir - it free. Ride on the wind, ride on the
Dm7 F/G E7 Am F/A C(add9)/G Fm6/A♭
30
wind, the wind of your dreams. When you find the clear, blue wa - ters
G7sus F/G C B♭ F(add9)
f
34
of the o - pen sea, Let your sail un - furl and you can
cresc.
B♭ F(add9) Gm11 F(add9)/A

o - pen sea,____ then set the course,____ set your spir - it free,____

o - pen sea,____ let your heart set the course,____ set your spir - it free____ as you

ride on the wind,____ ride on the wind, the wind of your

ride on the wind,____ the wind of your

Risseldy, Rosseldy

PUPIL'S PAGE 264

Texas Folk Song
Piano Accompaniment by Mark Brymer

Introduction not on Pupil's page **Verse**

1. I mar - ried my wife in the month of June,
2. She combed her hair but once a year,
3. She kept her shoes on the pan - try shelf,

Ris - sel - dy, ros - sel - dy, Mow, mow mow.

I car - ried her off in a
If you want an - y - more you can

sil - ver spoon,
shed a tear,
sing it your - self,

Ris - sel - dy, ros - sel - dy, Mow, mow, mow.

Refrain

Ris - sel - dy, ros - sel - dy, hey bom - bas - sit - y, Nick - et - y, nack - et - y,

Ret - ric - al qual - i - ty, Wil - low - by, wal - lo - by, Mow, mow, mow.

River of My People

PUPIL'S PAGE 176

Words and Music by Pete Seeger
Music based on Traditional Russian Folk Song
Piano Accompanmiment by Mark Brymer

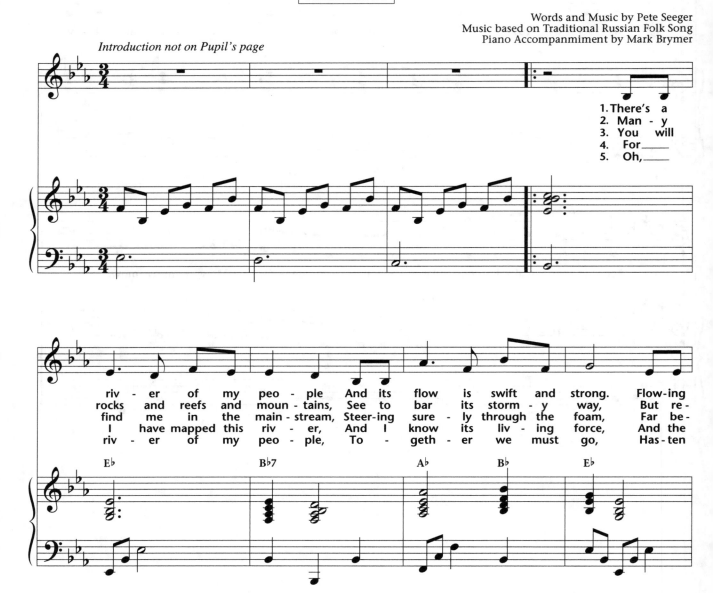

Introduction not on Pupil's page

1. There's a
2. Man - y
3. You will
4. For____
5. Oh,____

riv - er of my peo - ple And its flow is swift and strong. Flow-ing
rocks and reefs and moun - tains, See to bar its storm - y way, But re -
find me in the main - stream, Steer-ing sure - ly through the foam, Far be -
I have mapped this riv - er, And I know its liv - ing force, And the
riv - er of my peo - ple, To - geth - er we must go, Has - ten

338

to some might-y o-cean, though its course is deep and long, Flow-ing
lent - less - ly this ri - ver, seeks its broth - ers in the sea, But re-
yond the rag - ing wa-ters, I can see our cer - tain home. Far be-
cour - age that this gives me, Will____ hold me to my course. And the
on - ward to that meet - ing, Where my broth - ers wait be - low. Has - ten

A♭   E♭   B♭7   E♭

to some might-y o-cean, Though its course is deep and long.
lent - less - ly this ri - ver, seeks its broth - ers in the sea.
yond the rag - ing wa-ters, I can see our cer - tain home.
cour - age that this gives me, Will____ hold me to my course.
on - ward to that meet - ing, Where my broth - ers wait be - low.

A♭   E♭   B♭7   E♭

A♭   E♭2   E♭

Rock Around the Clock

PUPIL'S PAGE 234

Words and Music by Max C. Freedman and Jimmy DeKnight
Piano Accompaniment by Mark Brymer

341

Guitar cranks as before 4 times

broad day-light,— we're gon-na rock, gon-na rock a-round— the clock— to-night—

D   Em7   A7♯5

1.

Big 360° rotation of extended R arm

2.

When the
When the
When it's
When the

D

D

Rock of Ages
(Ma'oz Tsur)

PUPIL'S PAGE 405

Jewish Folk Song
Piano Accompaniment by Larry Moore

Introduction not on Pupil's page

ma oz tsur yε shu a ti lε xa na e lε sha be ax
Rock of ag - es, all our days, We fill the air with____ songs of praise.

ti kon beit tε fi la ti vε sham to da nε za be ax lε
All our foes thou will as - sail. Thy strength and pow - er____ will not fail. We'll

343

et   ta xin mat   be   ax,   mi tsar ha na   be   ax
de - di - cate   the   al - tar,   Faith will nev - er   fal - ter.

az eg mɔɾ bɛ   shir miz mɔɾ   xa nu kat ha miz   be   ax   be   ax
With our house of prayer re - stored,   Fill the air with____ hymns of praise.   hymns of praise.

Roll de Ole Chariot Along

PUPIL'S PAGE 243

African American Spiritual
Adapted by René Boyer-Alexander
Piano Accompaniment by Anna Marie Spallina

Refrain

Roll de ole char - i - ot a - long,____ Roll de ole char - i - ot a - long,____ Roll de ole char - i - ot a - long,____ Ef yo' don't hang on be - hin'. hin'.

1., 2. *To Verse*   3.   **Fine**

345

Verse

1. We are trav - el - in' from man - sions, man - sions, man - sions;
2. Ef yo' mud - der want to go, she shall wear a star - ry crown; Ef yo'

Trav - el - in' from man - sions, man - sions, man - sions; Trav - el - in' from man - sions,
mud - der want to go, she shall wear a star - ry crown; Ef yo' mud - der want to go, she shall

D.C. al Fine

man - sions, man - sions, You must hang on be - hin'.
wear a star - ry crown, And she must hang on be - hin'.

Round and Round

PUPIL'S PAGE 104

Anonymous
Piano Accompaniment by Mark Brymer

Introduction not on Pupil's page

Round and round the

Dm   Am   C   Dm   Dm   Am

Earth__ is turn - ing turn - ing al - ways round__ to morn - ing,

C   Dm   Dm   F   G   Dm

and from morn - ing round____ to night.

C   Dm   G   C   Am   Dm

Harmonization for unison only

Sakura
(Cherry Blossoms)

PUPIL'S PAGE 14

Japanese Folk Song
English Version by MMH
Piano Accompaniment by MMH

348

Salamanca Market

PUPIL'S PAGE 247

Words and Music by Mary Goetze
Piano Accompaniment by Anna Marie Spallina

Harmonization for unison only

Samba de Orfeu
(Dance of Orpheus)

PUPIL'S PAGE 190

Words by Antonio Maria
Music by Luiz Bonfa
Piano Accompaniment by Ben Scholz

Rhythmic

Portuguese: Que-ro vi-ver,____ que - ro__ sam - bar

B♭M7

A - té sen-tir__ a es - sen-cia da vi - da, Me fal-tar____

B♭M7

Cm7

Que - ro sam - bar,____ que - ro__ vi - ver,

Cm7

De - pois do sam - ba, ta bem, Meu a - mor pos - so mor - rer.

Cm7   F7   B♭M7

Que - ro vi - ver.___ mor, pos - so mor - rer.___   Quem quí -

B♭6   B♭

zer   gos - tar de mim,___   Se qui - zer

Fm7   B♭7   E♭M7   E♭6   E♭m7

vai - ser as - sim._____ Va - mos vi - ver,_____

va - mos____ sam - bar   Se a fan ta - sia_____ ras - gar, Meu a -

mor eu com - pro ou - tra   Va - mos sam - bar_____

va - mos___ vi - ver.   O sam - ba é___ livre,   Eu sou livre tam-

bem,   A - té   mor - rer._____

Scraping Up Sand

PUPIL'S PAGE 248

New England Folk Song
Piano Accompaniment by Ben Scholz

Scrap-ing up sand from the bot-tom of the sea, Shi-loh, Shi-loh,

Scrap-ing up sand from the bot-tom of the sea, Shi-loh, Li-za Jane.

Oh, how I love her, Oh, Li-za Jane,

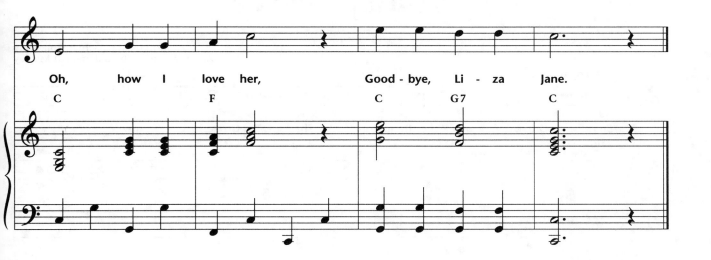

Oh, how I love her, Good-bye, Li - za Jane.

C   F   C   G7   C

Shady Grove

Southern Appalachian Folk Song
Piano Accompaniment by Bill and Pat Medley

Refrain

Shad - y Grove, my lit - tle love, Shad - y Grove, I know,

Shad - y Grove, my lit - tle love, Bound for Shad - y Grove.

Verse

1. Cheeks as red as the bloom - ing rose, Eyes of the deep - est brown;
2. Went to see my Shad - y Grove, She was stand - ing in the door,
3. Wish I had a big fine horse, Corn to____ feed him on,
4. Shad - y Grove, my lit - tle love, Shad - y Grove, I say,

You are the dar - ling of my heart, Stay till the sun goes down.
Shoes and stock - ings in her hand, Lit - tle bare____ feet on the floor.
Pret - ty - lit - tle girl, stay at home, Feed him____ when I'm gone.
Shad - y Grove,____ my lit - tle love, Don't wait till the Judg - ment Day!

356

Shibolet Basadeh
(Wheat in the Field)

PUPIL'S PAGE 424

Words and Music by Matiyahu Shelem
English Words by Linda Worsley
Piano Accompaniment by Ben Scholz

357

The Ship in Distress

PUPIL'S PAGE 211

English Ballad
Piano Accompaniment by Ben Scholz

1. You sail - ors bold who___ plough the o - cean. See
2. For four - teen days, heart - sore and hun - gry, see-ing
3. A full - dressed ship like the sun a - glit 'ring came

dan - ger lands - men___ nev - er know. It's not for ho - nor___
but wild wa - ter and___ bit - ter sky, Poor fel - lows, they stood___
bear - ing down___ to___ their re - lief. As soon as this glad___

or pro - mo - tion; No tongue can tell what they___ un - der - go. In the
in a tot - ter, A - cast - ing lots to which___ should___ die. The___
news was shout - ed, It ban - ished all their___ care and grief. The___

blus - t'rous___ wind and the gray dark wa - ter. Our
lot___ it___ fell on___ Rob - ert Jack - son whose
ship___ brought___ to, no - long - er drift - ing, Safe

F6   Am   Dm   Am

ship went drift - ing on the___ sea, Her
fam - i - ly was so ve - ry___ great. "I'm
in St. Vin - cent, Cape Ver - de she gained. You

Dm   Am   C   Am   Dm

rud - der___ bro - ken which brought us to ex - tre - mi - ty.
oh, my___ com - rades, Let me keep look - out 'til break of day.
hear my___ stor - y pray you'll nev - er suf - fer the like a - gain.

G   Am   F   Am   Dm

D.S.

Shoes of John

PUPIL'S PAGE 246

Southern Highlands Folk Song
Piano Accompaniment by Ben Scholz

Introduction not on Pupil's page

1. I am stand-ing in the shoes of
(2.) fit me, I will put them

John. I am stand-ing in the shoes of John. I am
on. If they fit me, I will put them on. If they

stand-ing, stand-ing, stand-ing, I am stand-ing, stand-ing, stand-ing, I am
fit me, fit me, fit me, If they fit me, fit me, fit me, If they

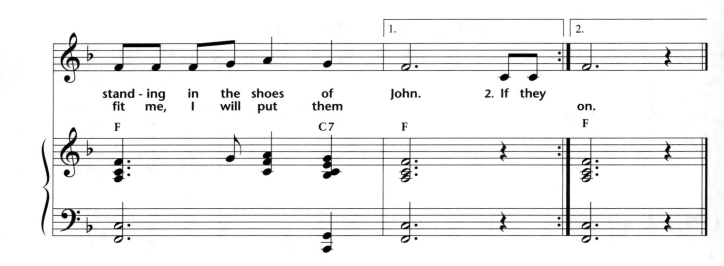

stand - ing   in   the   shoes   of   John.   2. If   they
fit   me,   I   will   put   of them   on.

Sing Hosanna

PUPIL'S PAGE 362

Words and Music by Michael Jothen
Arranged by Ben Scholz

high - est!— Now is the time— to sing. Lift up your voice,

Lift up your voice now in song!

Sing Ho - san - na, sing— Ho - san - na, Sing Ho - san - na,

sing — Ho - san - na, Sing Ho - san - na, Al - le - lu -

ia.

Now is the time — to sing. Lift up your voice, Lift up your voice now in

Sing Ho - san - na, Al - le - lu -

song!

ia.

Slap That Bass

PUPIL'S PAGE 146

Words by Ira Gershwin
Music by George Gershwin
Piano Accompaniment by Ben Scholz

Moderately
Introduction not on Pupil's page

Refrain

Slap that bass, slap it till it's diz-zy, Slap that bass, Keep the rhy-thm bus-y!

Zoom! zoom! zoom! Mis-e-ry you got to go!____

368

Slap that bass, Use it like a ton-ic! Slap that bass, Keep your Phil-har-mon-ic!

F7   A♭9   F7   D7

Zoom! zoom! zoom! And the milk and hon-ey-'ll flow!_____ Dic -

C   E♭9   Gm   F   G7   C7   Gm6   C7

ta - tors would be___ bet-ter off___ if they zoom zoomed now and then.___ To -

F   F6   G7   C6   C9

day_____ you can see___ that the hap - pi - est men

F   F6   G7   CM7

All got rhy-thm! In which case If you want to bub-ble, Slap that bass,

Slap a-way your trou-ble! Learn to zoom, zoom, zoom! Slap that

bass! bass!

Sometimes I Feel
Like a Motherless Child

PUPIL'S PAGE 271

African American Spiritual
Piano Accompaniment by Ben Scholz

1. Some - times I feel like a moth - er - less child,___
2. Some - times I feel like I'm al - most gone,___

Some-times I feel like a moth - er - less child,___
Some-times I feel like I'm al - most gone,___

Some-times I feel like a moth - er - less child,___
Some-times I feel like I'm al - most gone,___

long   way___ from   home,_____ A

long   way___ from   home.

The Stars and Stripes Forever

PUPIL'S PAGE 390

Words and Music by John Philip Sousa
Piano Accompaniment by Ben Scholz

*Interlude: March 8 counts, 4-point pivot, march 4 counts, 2-point pivot, march 4 counts
Optional: Pull out flags for verse 2

The Star-Spangled Banner

PUPIL'S PAGE 386

Music Attributed to J. S. Smith
Words by Francis Scott Key
Piano Accompaniment by Dean Crocker

In Strict Tempo

Introduction not on Pupil's page

1. Oh,_____ say, can you see, by the dawn's ear - ly light, What so
2. On the shore, dim - ly seen through the mists of the deep, Where the
3. Oh,_____ thus be it ev-er when_____ free men shall stand Be -

proud - ly we hailed at the twi - light's last gleam - ing? Whose broad
foe's haugh - ty host in dread si - lence re - pos - es, What is
tween their loved homes and the war's des - o - la - tion! Blest with

Verses 2 and 3 are in Teacher's Edition

stripes and bright stars, through the per - li - ous fight, O'er the ram - parts we
that which the breeze, o'er the tow - er - ing steep, As it fit - ful - ly
vic - t'ry and peace, may the heav'n res - cued land Praise the Pow'r that hath

watched were so gal - lant - ly stream - ing? And the rock - ets' red glare, the bombs
blows, half con - ceals, half dis - clos - es? Now it catch - es the gleam of the
made and pre - served us a na - tion. Then___ con - quer we must, for our

burst - ing in air, Gave proof through the night that our flag was still
morn - ing' first beam, In full glo - ry re - flect - ed now___ shines on the
cause it is just, And this be our mot - to, "In___ God is our

there. Oh, say, does that__ Star - Span - gled Ban - ner__ yet__ wave__ O'er the
steam; 'Tis the Star - Span - gled__ Ban - ner, oh, long may__ it__ wave__ O'er the
trust." And the Star - Span - gled__ Ban - ner in tri - umph__ shall__ wave__ O'er the

land_____ of the free and the home of the brave?
land_____ of the free and the home of the brave?
land_____ of the free and the home of the brave?

Sugar in the Gourd

PUPIL'S PAGE 251

Southern Folk Song
Piano Accompaniment by Ben Scholz

Introduction not on Pupil's page

1. Met her on the road, she danced on the board,
2. Had a lit - tle chick-en, she had a wood - en leg,
3. I___ went___ down in the old clay___ field,

Played a lit - tle tune called "Sug - ar in the Gourd."
Best___ lit - tle chick-en that ev - er laid an egg.
Black - snake___ grabbed me by___ the___ heel.

378

Sug - ar in the gourd___ and I can't get it out,
Laid more eggs than an - y hen a - round the___ farm,
I___ turned a - round___ just to do my___ best, And

D   A7

Way to get the sug - ar out is roll the gourd a - bout.
Have to keep that chick - en and her eggs from an - y harm.
drove___ my___ head in - to a hor - net's___ nest.

D   A7   D

Suliram

PUPIL'S PAGE 58

Indonesian Folk Song
Arranged by Raymond J. Malone
English Words by Audrey Snyder
Piano Accompaniment by Ben Scholz

a - du hai in - dung se - o - rang.
how we've longed, we've longed for you to come,

Bi - jak - lak sa - na di - pan - dang ma - nis.
and now we've found you, we'll nev - er let you go.

Suomen Salossa
(The Finnish Forest)

PUPIL'S PAGE 422

Finnish Folk Song
English Words by Linda Worsley
Piano Accompaniment by Ben Scholz

Introduction not on Pupil's page

Finnish: **Hon - ka - en**
English: **Deep in the**

kess - kel - lä mök - ki - ni sei - soo, Suo - me - ni

pines of the green leaf - y for - est, There in Su -

so - re - as - sa sa - los - sa, Hon - ka - en

o - mi - land, my cot - tage stands. Light spark - 'ling

383

välil - tä siin ta - vä sel - kä
'round from the dawn soft - ly break - ing,

G   C   D

Vilk - ku - vi ko - it - te - hen va - los - sa.   Hoi
Here in Su - o - mi - land, the fair - est of lands.   Hoi

D   Em   A7   D7   G

laa - ri laa - ri laa,   Hoi laa - ri laa - ri laa,   Hoi
laa - ri laa - ri laa,   Hoi laa - ri laa - ri laa,   Hoi

D7

pp echo   *f*

laa - ri laa - ri laa,   Hoi laa - ri laa - ri laa,
laa - ri laa - ri laa,   Hoi laa - ri laa - ri laa,

Kai - ku mun su - loi - nen Suo - me - ni maa!
Joy - ful the song of our fair na - tive land!

Sweet and Low

PUPIL'S PAGE 184

Words by Alfred Tennyson
Music by Joseph Barnby
Piano Accompaniment by Ben Scholz

Bring him a - gain to me._____ While my lit - tle one,

Am   E7   F   A♭7   C   G7

while   my   pret - ty   one   sleeps.

C   G7   C

Tain't What You Do

Words and Music by Sy Oliver and James Young
Piano Accompaniment by Ben Scholz

1. Tain't what you do, it's the way that cha do it. Tain't what you do, it's the way that cha do it.

Pupil book repeats

Tain't what you do, it's the way that cha do it, that's what gets— re-sults.—

2. Tain't what you say, it's the way that cha say it. Tain't what you say, it's the way that cha say it.

Tain't what you say, it's the way that cha say it, That's what gets— re-sults.— You can

try hard,— don't mean a thing.— Take it

ea - sy⎯⎯ then your jive will swing.⎯⎯

3. Tain't what you do, it's the way that cha do it. Tain't what you do, it's the way that cha do it.

Tain't what you do, it's the way that cha do it, that's what gets⎯⎯ re-sults.⎯⎯

That Great Come and Get It Day

PUPIL'S PAGE 306

Words by E.Y. Harburg
Music by Burton Lane
Piano Accompaniment by Dean Crocker

fun when wor-ry is done and mon-ey is hay?_____ That's the

time things will come your way on that

great, great come and get it day. I'll get my

gal _____ that cal-i-co gown. I'll get my

mule _____ that a-cre of groun', 'cause word has

come _____ from Ga-bri-el's horn, the earth be-

Pupil's Edition repeats

great   come and get it day,   won't it be

fun when wor-ry is   done and mon-ey is   hay?_____   That's the

time   things will come your   way   on that

great,___ great___ come and get it and keep it, and share it,

great, great, come and get it day!_____

Slowly

There Was a Blue Flower

PUPIL'S PAGE 219

Words and Music by Libby Larsen
Piano Accompaniment by Ben Scholz

flower_____ grow - ing all a - lone. So he

moved,_____ he moved to a place far a - way._____

Where am I go - ing he said I'll go to the moun - tains

I'll   go to the moun-tains,   may-be   some blue___ flowers   live

there.   and   so   the blue flower left   to   live   in the moun - tains

When he ar - rived   he saw man - y   blue_____   flowers.

He was hap-py, so hap-py to see the col-or of his dreams

and when he met them_____ he got a - long with them.

They____ liked him and he liked them.____

And he was nev - er, ev - er sad a - gain.

There Was a Jolly Miller

PUPIL'S PAGE 250

New England Folk Song
Piano Accompaniment by Ben Scholz

There was a jol-ly mil-ler and he lived by him-self, As the wheel went 'round he made his wealth; With one hand in the hop-per and the oth-er in the bag, As the wheel went 'round he made his grab.

They Call the Wind Maria

PUPIL'S PAGE 312

Words by Alan Jay Lerner
Music by Frederick Loewe
Piano Accompaniment by Dean Crocker

405

fi - re. The rain is Tess, the fire is Jo, and they
whin - in,' I had a girl, and she had me. And the

call the wind Ma - ri - a.   Ma - ri - a blows the
sun was al - ways shin - in.'   But then one day I

stars a - round and sends the clouds a - fly - in'.   Ma-
left my girl. I left her far be - hind me. And

ri - a makes the moun - tains sound like folks were up there
now I'm lost, so gol - durn lost, like not e - ven God can

dy - in'. }
find me. }
Ma - ri - a!_____ Ma -

ri - a!_____ They call the wind Ma -

ri - a!_____ Be ri - a!_____ Ma -

ri - a!_____ Ma - ri - a!_____ They

call the wind Ma - ri - a!

This Pretty Planet

PUPIL'S PAGE 194

Words and Music by John Forster and Tom Chapin
Adapted by MMH
Piano Accompaniment by Ben Scholz

Introduction not on Pupil's page

Vocal harmony in Pupil's book works with this accompaniment.

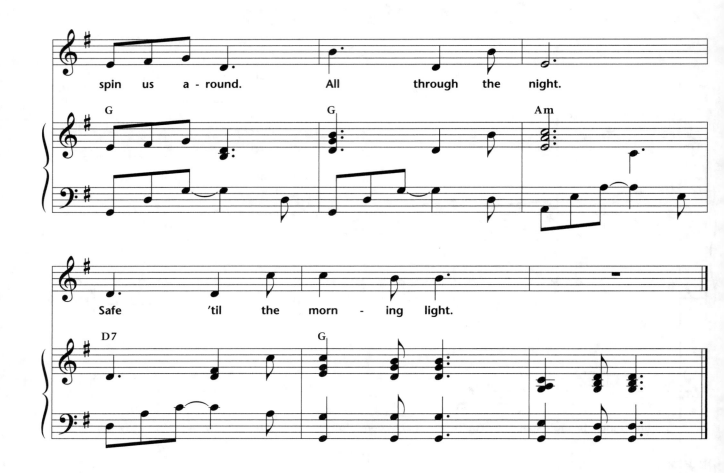

spin us a - round. All through the night.

Safe 'til the morn - ing light.

Tina Singu

PUPIL'S PAGE 36

Song from Lesotho
As Sung by Kathleen Hill
Piano Accompaniment by Carol Jay

Sotho: Ti - na sing - u le - lu - vu - tae — o. Wat - sha, wat - sha,

wat - sha, Ti - na, Ti - na sing - u

le - lu - vu - tae — o. Wat - sha, wat - sha, wat - sha.

Troika

PUPIL'S PAGE 230

Additional Words and Music by Dave and Jean Perry
Based on a Traditional Russian Folk Song
Piano Accompaniment by Ben Scholz

Hur - ry, coach - man, with the troi - ka, hur - ry, hors - es, through the snow,

To the win - ter cel - e - bra - tion, to the vil - lage far be - low.

The Trout

PUPIL'S PAGE 342

Words and Music by Franz Schubert
Arranged by Ed Harris
Piano Accompaniment by Ben Scholz

1. One day as I was walk - ing be -

side a clear sun-ny stream, I spied a trout so dash - ing, an

Measure numbers do not match Pupil Edition

415

all so fair and good.

Pupil Edition repeats

mf

2. A fish - er - man came near me and

bold - ly stood up on the shore. He had a string of fish, yet he

trout can-not be caught.

This fish - er was no sports - man,

he had a scheme;

he made the wa - ter ver - y

he made the wa - ter

muddy and cast——— in-to the stream. And when he reeled his

line in, he caught——— my fish and pulled him out. My

heart was filled with sor - row at how he tricked the trout; my

heart_ was filled_ with_ sor - row at how he tricked the trout.

Tsing Chun U Chü
(Youth Dance Song)

PUPIL'S PAGE 272

Taiwanese Folk Song
Collected and Transcribed by Kathy B. Sorenson
Piano Accompaniment by Bill and Pat Medley

Pronunciation: tai yang sia shan ming jau yi jiu pa shang lai
English: **Though the sun has dis- ap- peared in - to the__ west,**

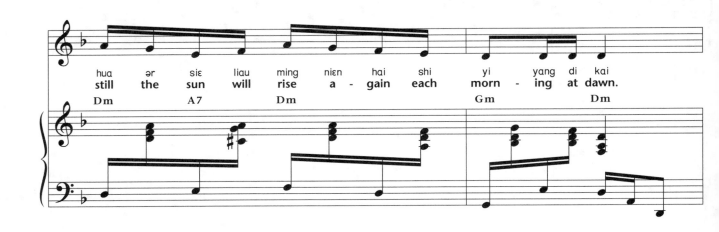

hua ər siɛ liau ming niɛn hai shi yi yang di kai
still the sun will rise a - gain each morn - ing at dawn.

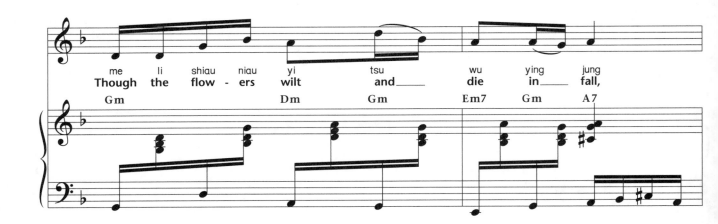

me li shiau niau yi tsu wu ying jung
Though the flow - ers wilt and__ die in__ fall,

Tum Balalaika

PUPIL'S PAGE 68

Traditional Russian Yiddish Song
Arranged by Jay Broeker
Piano Accompaniment by Ben Scholz

Introduction not on Pupil's page

1. Maid - en, maid - en, tell___ me true.
2. Lis - ten, I've an an - swer for you,

What can grow with - out___ the dew?
stones can grow with - out___ the dew.

What___ can burn for
Love___ can burn for

Refrain

years___ and years?
years___ and years,

What___ can cry and shed___ no tears?
Hearts___ can cry and shed___ no tears.

Vem Kan Segla
(Who Can Sail?)

PUPIL'S PAGE 419

Folk Song from Åland,
a Swedish-speaking Island of Finland
English Words by Linda Worsley
Piano Accompaniment by Ben Scholz

426

The Wabash Cannonball

Words and Music by William Kindt
Piano Accompaniment by Ben Scholz

v1: Point R
v2: Add on train steps facing L (6 groups)
v3: Add on train steps facing R
v4: Hold belt buckle and rock hips side to side

427

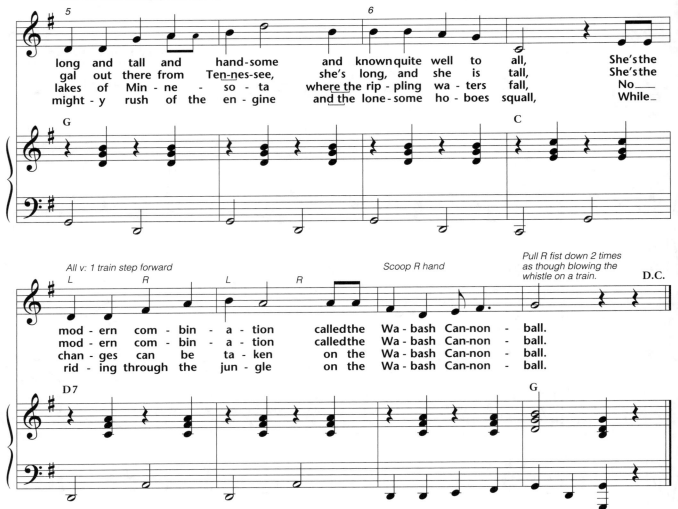

Wachet auf
(Waken Now)

PUPIL'S PAGE 259

Words and Music by Johann Jacob Wachsmann
English words by MMH
Piano Accompaniment by Bill and Pat Medley

Ostinato is found in Teacher's Edition

Waiting for Life

PUPIL'S PAGE 292

Music by Stephen Flaherty
Words by Lynn Ahrens
Piano Accompaniment by Ben Scholz

430

far.

Girl 1

How it must feel__ to go rac - ing where-ev - er you please,

The Workers come to life,
their movement accenting the beats
Encourage levels

Storytellers

Oo la, oo la,

fly - ing as free__ as a bird__ with its tail__ in the

oo la, oo la.

racing down the beach, racing to pla - ces

I was meant to reach! My stran - ger! One

day you'll ar - rive. Your car will stop and in I'll hop and off we'll

Ti Moune's arms open like spread wings, L arm up, R arm down

She "flies" around the stage, arms outstretched

drive.. we'll

drive!

All circle around Ti Moune

Oh, gods, oh gods, let me fly!

Ti Moune sits

Send me to pla - ces where no___ one be - fore___ me has been.

Walk by the River

PUPIL'S PAGE 74

Words and Music by Holly Turnquist Fischer
Piano Accompaniment by Warren Stine

1. If you have a bur-den that's too heav-y a load,___
2. Come down to the riv-er, bring your trou-bles a-long.___

come down to the riv-er, and we'll set it a-float.___
Let the rush-ing wa-ters weave them in-to a song.___

Let the wa-ters car-ry it right out to the sea,_____ and
Sing a-bout your trou-bles and be-fore ver-y long_____ you will

sing by the riv-er with our voic-es mak-ing har-mo-ny in

G   C   D

notes so sweet and fine_____ that will

Em   C   C7   N.C.

ech-o down the riv-er for a ver-y long__ time._____

G   C   G

The Water Is Wide

English Folk Song
Arranged by Luigi Zaninelli
Piano Accompaniment by Ben Scholz

1. The wa - ter is wide, _____ I can - not get

sail-ing on the sea, She's load-ed deep_____ as deep can

be, But not so deep_____ as the love I'm in;

I care not if_____ I sink or swim.

Wayfaring Stranger

PUPIL'S PAGE 283

Southern Folk Hymn
Piano Accompaniment by Ben Scholz

there   to see my Fa - ther,___ I'm go - ing there   no more to

roam.   I'm just a - go -   ing o - ver Jor - dan,___   I'm on - ly

go   -   ing o - ver home.

When I Sing

PUPIL'S PAGE 44

Words and Music by Bill Henderson
Arranged by David J. Elliott
Piano Accompaniment by Ben Scholz

Why We Tell the Story

PUPIL'S PAGE 303

Music by Stephen Flaherty
Words by Lynn Ahrens
Piano Accompaniment by Ben Scholz

All raise arms as Ti Moune
stands up on the chair or
block, throwing her arms up

Ti Moune

All lower arms

Daniel

Ooh,_____ ooh - way_

___ ooh._____

And she

stands a-gainst_ the light - ning and_ the thun - der,_

And she

Daniel, looking at Ti Moune, throws his arms up to her

Daniel slowly lowers his hands

Group 1

Group 2

shel- ters and_ pro- tects _ us from_ a - bove, and she

All throw arms up to Ti Moune

fills us with_ the pow - er and_ the won - der_ of____ her

All stand and slowly lower arms

love._____ And this_ is

455

Winter Ade
(G Major)

PUPIL'S PAGE 132

German Folk Melody
Piano Accompaniment by Ben Scholz

German: Win - ter A - de schei - den - tut weh,
English: Win - ter, fare - well! part - ing is sad;

a - ber dein Schei - den macht, dass mir das
But when at last you de - part, dass your leav - ing

Her - ze - lacht, Win - ter a - de,
cheers my____ heart, Win - ter, fare - well!

Win - ter a - de.
Win - ter, fare - well!

459

Winter Ade
(G Minor)

PUPIL'S PAGE 133

German Folk Melody
Piano Accompaniment by Ben Scholz

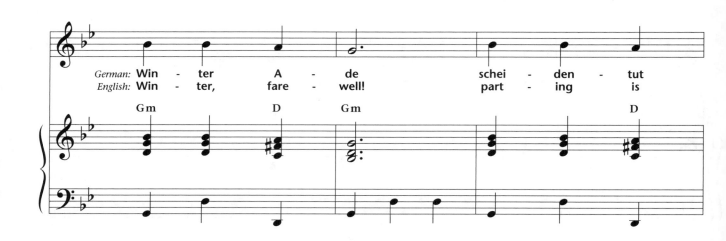

German: Win - ter A - de schei - den - tut
English: Win - ter, fare - well! part - ing is

weh, a - ber dein Schei - den macht,
sad; But when at last you de - part,

dass mir das Her - ze - lacht, Win - ter a -
your leav - ing cheers my_____ heart, Win - ter, fare -

de, Win - ter a - de.
well! Win - ter, fare - well!

Wondering

PUPIL'S PAGE 282

Bohemian Folk Song
Piano Accompaniment by Steve Hoover

1. Where are the clouds that were here last night?
2. How far a - way is the dis - tant sky?

Why does the moon give a sil - v'ry light?
How do we know which is you or I?

Who can tell?
Who can tell?

Who can say? When will to - mor - row be yes - ter - day?
Who can say? How man - y miles would be far a - way?

Yellow Bird

PUPIL'S PAGE 154

Words and Music by Irving Burgie
Piano Accompaniment by Dean Crocker

Introduction not on Pupil's page

Costumed "bird" struts around the stage, flapping wings and "flying" around and about rest of cast. Chorus in stand-by position.

My friend has a yel - low bird___ that goes with him___ for a

walk, but e - ven more than that, __ it

*More costumed "birds" enter and strut around stage.
Or, place cardboard or puppet birds on lone bamboo
poles that dancers manuveur around the stage.*

al - so knows __ how to talk. Yel - low

bird, high up in co - co - nut tree.

Yel - low bird, come back an' an - swer for me. I would like___ to know, how do flow - ers grow?

(Chorus begins these actions)
Point thumbs to self *Shrug*

Can you tell___ me when sum - mer comes___ a - gain?

Clasp hands like begging *Shrug*

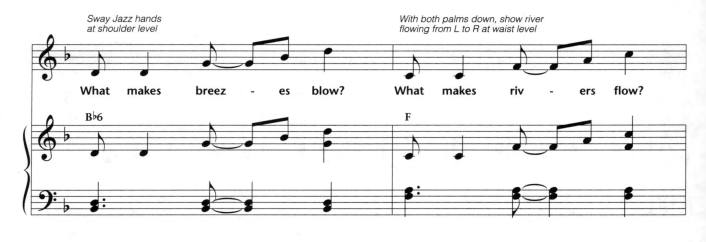

Sway Jazz hands at shoulder level   *With both palms down, show river flowing from L to R at waist level*

What makes breez - es blow? What makes riv - ers flow?

B♭6   F

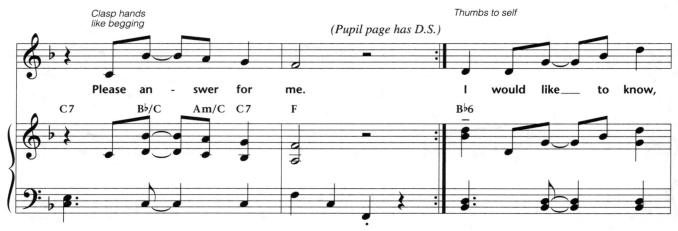

Clasp hands like begging   *(Pupil page has D.S.)*   *Thumbs to self*

Please an - swer for me.   I would like___ to know,

C7   B♭/C   Am/C   C7   F   B♭6

Shrug   *Clasp hands like begging*   *Shrug*

how do flow - ers grow? Can you tell___ me when sum - mer comes___ a - gain?

F   C7   F   F/A

Sway Jazz hands at shoulder level

With both palms down, show river flowing from L to R at waist level

What makes breez - es blow? What makes riv - ers flow?

1st time: Clasp begging hands to the L
2nd time: Clasp begging hands to the R

Please an - swer for me.

Clasp begging hands center near chest

Please an - swer for me.

Yerakina

PUPIL'S PAGE 216

Introduction not in Pupil's Page

Greek Folk Song

Pronunciation: ki ni se i ye ra
English: **Yer - a - ki - na went for wa - ter, When she fell in to the**

ki na yia ne ro kri o na
well and cried___ out, I ran to___ see.___ Then I heard her

fe ri droum droum droum droum droum droum ta vra
man - y brace-lets jan - gle droom droom droom droom___ droom. "Yer-a - ki - na,

468

hio lia tis vron doun droum droum droum droum droum droum
I will save your life," droom___ droom___ droom droom droom droom___

droum ta vra hio lia tis vron drun
droom, "And I will then take you for my___ wife!"___

You Sing for Me

PUPIL'S PAGE 106

Words and Music by Raymond K. McLain
Piano Accompaniment by Bill and Pat Medley

Introduction not in Pupil's Edition

Verse

1. I've come through storm-y weath-er, I'm sure you've seen it too. but
2. I'll nev-er be more read-y to sing a-long with you. To

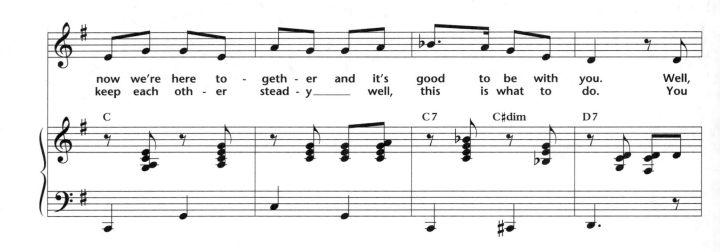

now we're here to - geth-er and it's good to be with you. Well,
keep each oth-er stead-y_____ well, this is what to do. You

here I am and there you are with noth - ing much to say.
lis - ten to the rhy - thm, then start mov - in' to the beat. Come

Sure - ly there's some bet - ter way to cel - e - brate to - day.
on, sweet mu - sic mak - er,___ let's give our - selves a treat. } You sing for

me,_____ I'll sing_ for you._____ We need each

You sing for me, I'll sing for you. We need each

Refrain

Yüe líang wan wan
(Crescent Moon)

Folk Song from China
Piano Accompaniment by Ben Scholz

Pronunciation: pao ma lio lio di shan shang i dwɔ lio lio di ün yo
English: Run - ning horse, to the moun-tain top, Lit - tle clouds in a clus - ter

duan duan lio lio di jao tsai kang dıng lio lio di chʌng yo
Face to face, the___ moon and cloud, fly a - cross___ the___ vil - lage,

üe liang wan wan kang dıng lio lio di chʌng yo
Pale moon, Curv-ing, curv - ing,___ Cres - cent moon___ o - ver Cheng Yo.

Acknowledgments

Grateful acknowledgement is given to the following authors, composers, and publishers. Every effort has been made to trace the ownership of all copyrighted material and to secure the necessary permissions to reprint these selections. In the case of some selections for which acknowledgment is not given, extensive research has failed to locate the copyright holders.

Songs and Speech Pieces

Angelina, Words and Music by Irving Burgie Copyright © 1960; Renewed 1988 Cherry Lane Music Publishing Company, Inc. (ASCAP), Lord Burgess Music Publishing (ASCAP) and DreamWorks Songs (ASCAP). Worldwide Rights for Lord Burgess Music Publishing and DreamWorks Songs Administered by Cherry Lane Music Publishing Company, Inc. International Copyright Secured. All Rights Reserved.

Bashana Haba 'Ah (In the Year to Come), Lyrics by Ehud Manor. Music by Nurit Hirsh. Copyright © 1970 (Renewed 1998) EMI SONGS (ISRAEL) LTD. All Rights Controlled and Administered by EMI BLACKWOOD MUSIC INC. All Rights Reserved, International Copyright Secured. Used by Permission.

Blue Suede Shoes, Words and Music by Carl Lee Perkins. Copyright © 1955, 1956 HI-LO MUSIC, INC. © Renewed 1983, 1984 CARL PERKINS MUSIC, INC. (Administered by WREN MUSIC CO., A Division of MPL Music Publishing, Inc.) All Rights Reserved.

Bop 'til You Drop, Words and Music by Douglas Colvin and John Cummings. Copyright © 1987 TACO TUNES. All Rights Administered by WB MUSIC CORP. All Rights Reserved. Used by Permission.

Camelot, from CAMELOT. Words by Alan Jay Lerner. Music by Frederick Loewe. Copyright © 1960, 1961 by Alan Jay Lerner and Frederick Loewe. Copyright Renewed. Chappell & Co. owner of publication and allied rights throughout the world. International Copyright Secured. All Rights Reserved.

Carol from an Irish Cabin, Words by Ruth Durand. Music by Dale Wood. Copyright © WARNER BROS. PUBLICATIONS U.S. INC. International Copyright Secured. All Rights Reserved.

Charleston, Words and Music by Cecil Mack and Jimmy Johnson. Copyright © 1923 (Renewed) WARNER BROS. INC. All Rights Reserved.

Choo Choo Ch' Boogie, Words and Music by Vaughn Horton, Denver Darling and Milton Gabler. Copyright © 1945 (Renewed) RYTVOC, INC. All Rights Reserved.

Comedy Tonight, From A FUNNY THING HAPPENED ON THE WAY TO THE FORUM. Words and Music by Stephen Sondheim. Copyright © 1962 by Stephen Sondheim. Copyright Renewed. Burthen Music Company, Inc. owner of publication and allied rights throughout the World. Chappell & Co. Sole Selling Agent. International Copyright Secured. All Rights Reserved.

Conga, Words and Music by Enrique Garcia. Copyright © 1985 FOREIGN IMPORTED PRODUCTIONS & PUBLISHING, INC. (BMI). International Copyright Secured. All Rights Reserved.

Cum-ma-la Be-stay, Words and Music by Donnie Burks, Jerry Vance and Terry Philips. Copyright © 1965 (Renewed 1993) by Donny Burke, Jerry Vance and Terry Philips. International Copyright Secured. All Rights Reserved.

Dancing in the Street, Words and Music by Marvin Gaye, Ivy Hunter and William Stevenson. Copyright © 1964 (Renewed 1992) FCG MUSIC, NMG MUSIC, MGIII MUSIC, JOBETE MUSIC CO., INC. and STONE AGATE MUSIC. All Rights Controlled and Administered by EMI APRIL MUSIC INC. and EMI BLACKWOOD MUSIC INC. on behalf of JOBETE MUSIC CO., INC. and STONE AGATE MUSIC (A Division of JOBETE MUSIC CO., INC.) All Rights Reserved. International Copyright Secured. Used by Permission.

Doctor Jazz, Words and Music by John Jacobson and Steve Zegree. Copyright © 2001 by HAL LEONARD CORPORATION. International Copyright Secured. All Rights Reserved.

Doing the Latest Rag, from TITANIC. Music and Lyrics by Maury Yeston. Copyright © 1994 Yeston Music Ltd. (BMI) Worldwide Rights for Yeston Music Ltd. Administered by Cherry River Music Co. International Copyright Secured. All Rights Reserved.

Earth Child, Words and Music by Sharon Burch. Copyright © by Canyon Records. International Copyright Secured. All Rights Reserved.

Teacher's Notes

Alphabetical Song Index